P9-DGS-334

TRAVEL — ADVENTURE

These are BORZOI BOOKS, *published by Alfred A. Knopf*

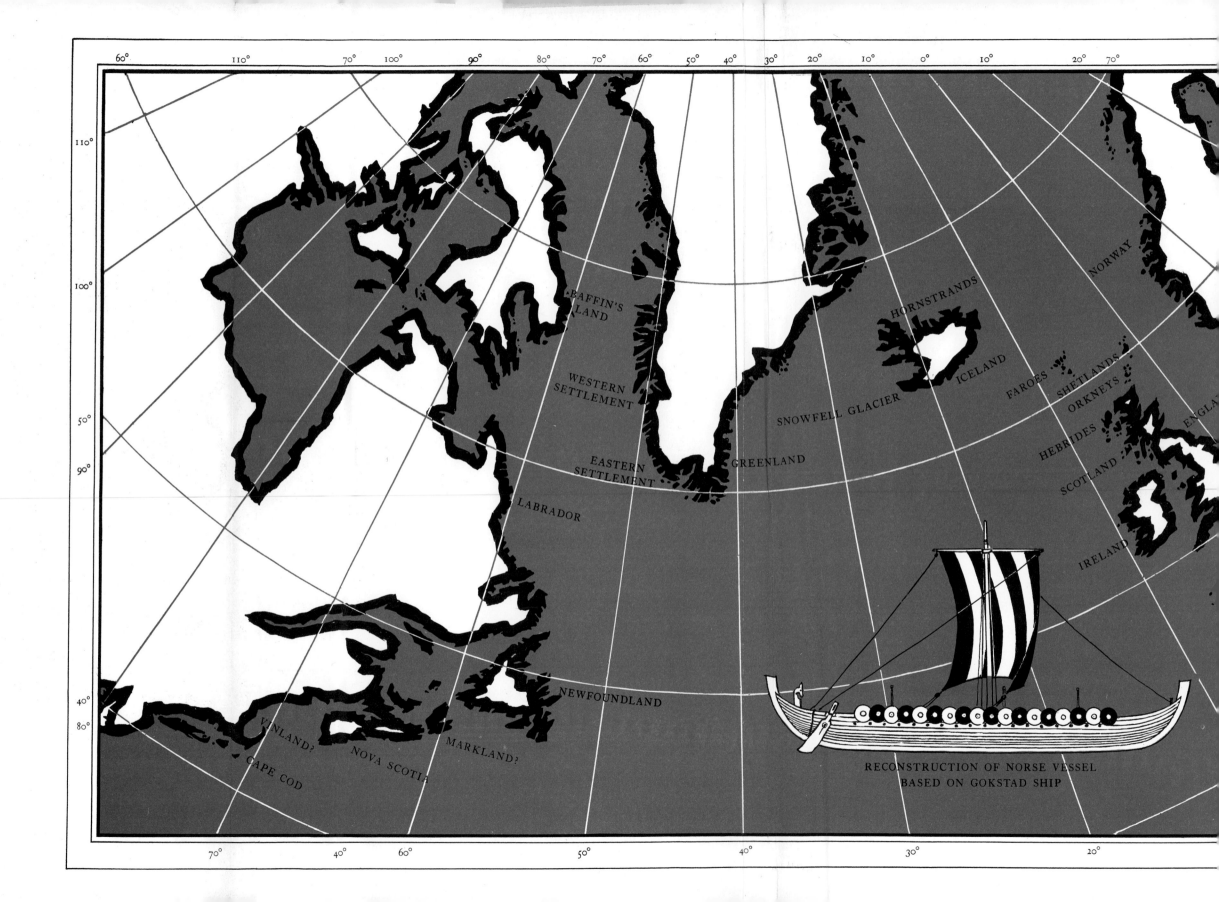

RECONSTRUCTION OF NORSE VESSEL
BASED ON GOKSTAD SHIP

VOYAGES TO VINLAND

The first American saga

VOYAGES TO VINLAND

The first American saga

newly translated and interpreted

by EINAR Ingvald HAUGEN, ed

Thompson Professor of Scandinavian Languages

University of Wisconsin ❁ *Illustrated by*

FREDERICK TRENCH CHAPMAN

ALFRED A. KNOPF ❁ 1942 ❁ NEW YORK

TO THE BRAVE NORSEMEN

OF OUR DAY

WHO SAIL THE COURSE OF LEIF AND ERIC

FOR THE FREEDOM OF THEIR NATIVE SOIL

FOREWORD

The American public has too long been led to believe, in the words of one obscure writer, that the Norse claim to American discovery and exploration " rests entirely upon tradition, poetic legends, and some slight circumstantial evidence." This view has been encouraged by the fact that most of the books which have been available to the general public on this subject are uncritical and wildly speculative. They use the known facts as springboards for imaginative flights and produce a justified reaction of skepticism in many of their readers. Those tomes, on the other hand, which present the facts solidly and without exaggeration are usually too learned or inaccessible for general reading. Through the agitation of various writers and Scandinavian groups in this country, a considerable interest has been awakened in the subject. But one is hard put to it when the request comes for further information. There is genuine need for a book that will present in readable form the text of the sagas dealing with the Norse discoveries, and sift out from the enormous scholarship of the subject those facts that seem well-established and give them a proper setting. It is hoped that this need may in some degree be met by the present book, which was made possible by a group of book-lovers and bookmakers in Chicago banded together under the name of " Holiday Press."

The reader should be triply warned before entering upon the *Saga of Vinland*.

First of all: this translation is a new one, made directly
from the original manuscripts of the thirteenth and fourteenth centuries as reproduced by A. M. Reeves. It was
made for the members of the Holiday Press with the inten-
tion of rendering the old sagas as vividly and understand-
ably as possible to modern readers. Samuel Laing's translation of a century ago, which appears in the Everyman's
Library, is antiquated; Reeves' translation of 1890 is stiff
and unreadable; G. Gathorne-Hardy's of 1924 is readable,
but distinctly British in idiom, besides being the property
of the Oxford Press. A new translation could be justified
only by the need for bringing before the American public
a clear, concise, readable version in the modern American
idiom. This saga is the earliest document of American
history, and if for no other reason, it deserves an American version.

But if it is done into modern American, one may ask,
are we not violating the spirit of the medieval documents?
This might be true, if they had been a part of the romantic
tradition of the Middle Ages. But the family sagas of Iceland are deeply rooted in the realism of everyday life.
They are plain, unadorned tales told by simple folk concerning authentic events in the lives of their own ancestors. Their style is straightforward and unvarnished, for
they were spoken before they were written. Many trans-
lators have outrageously violated their spirit by turning
them into romantic, medieval English, as if they were
tales of King Arthur and his noble knights. The sagas
come from another and humbler sphere: they are the
stories of sailors and adventurers, merchants and farmers,
shepherds and fishermen, told with the humor and the
simplicity of the common man. We who live today can
best enter into their world if they are allowed to speak to
us in the simple, direct accents of our own day. The trans-

lator has not sought to vulgarize them by making them slangy or jocular, but has used modern and colloquial idioms wherever these seemed to render the spirit of the original.

Where Laing translated, " Now we have two occupations to attend to," and Reeves wrote, " We will now divide our labors," this translator says, " From now on we have two jobs on our hands." Where Reeves translated, " The wind waxed amain," this version puts it, " A storm blew up." According to Reeves, Leif says to the straying Tyrker, " Wherefore art thou so belated, foster-father mine, and astray from the others? " The hearty Leif would not have recognized this artificial speech as his own; he simply said, " Why were you so late, foster-father, and how did you get parted from your company? " It would not have occurred to the unlucky Thorvald to speak in these lofty terms: " I counsel you now to retrace your way with the utmost speed." His speech is simple and unaffected: " I advise you to make ready for your return as quickly as possible."

Another step in making these stories presentable to the lay reader has been the harmonization of the two versions. We shall get no real feeling of the impression made on the Norsemen by their discoveries unless we allow the two versions to supplement rather than contradict one another. In the opinion of the present writer both of them go back to men who were familiar with the original events, and each has preserved certain facets of these events. So they have here been combined into a coherent account of the Norse discoveries somewhat in the manner of G. Gathorne-Hardy's version. The manuscripts have been closely followed, but certain episodes and statements that would only confuse the lay reader have boldly been omitted, while valuable items from other sources have some-

times been inserted in the text. Any one who is interested
in re-examining the problems of the text will in any case
have to go to the magnificent edition of A. M. Reeves. Our
interest here has been to weld out of the manuscripts a
true Saga of Vinland. In so doing we are not far from the
practice of Iceland's ancient saga scribes, who listened to
different versions of the same story and then used their
own judgments in creating a coherent, probable account.

A third step in making the saga acceptable to the American reader has been our policy of treating the rather difficult Icelandic names. One of the most discouraging aspects
of the sagas to a modern reader is their extreme fondness
for lists of names, many of which sound alike and confuse
the story. Here, again, consistency has given way to the
needs of the reader. Some of these names have long been
familiar in English, and have acquired traditional forms.
It would be foolish to write *Olafr* or *Thorr,* when these
are well-known under the simpler forms of " Olaf " and
" Thor."

The name of our hero Leif has aroused more ardent
controversy than that of any other character. The form
here presented is *Leif Ericson.* Some of the other contend-
ers, all vehemently championed by various schools of
thought, are *Leifr* or *Leiv* for the given name, and *Ericsson, Erickson, Erikson, Eriksson, Eriksen,* or *Eiriksson* for
the patronymic. Most of these bear the mark of modern
Scandinavian sound developments. For our purposes the
only real problem involved is this: shall we retain the
original form of the name unchanged, or shall we give it
a more acceptable English form? In Old Norse it was generally written *Leifr Eiriksson,* though Hauksbók is the
only one of the three manuscripts of this saga that does so;
AM 557 4to writes *Eireksson* and Flateyarbók *Æireksson.*
But the name *Eirikr* was borrowed into English a long

time ago in the form *Eric*. Through long usage this form has become as natural to English as *Erik* is to modern Scandinavian. In English, also, the ending *-son* is always added directly to a name, without intervening *s*. This leaves us with only two choices in English: either the original Leifr Eiriksson or the anglicized Leif Ericson. All the other forms are based on modern Scandinavian speech habits and have no special relevance for English. But just as Christopher Columbus bears a traditionally anglicized name instead of his original one, so Leif is best presented in English form. The needs of the reader are best served by a form that rolls most easily from the tongue, when this is one that does not violate the spirit of the original. It is hoped that this form may be widely adopted, to eliminate the confusion which drove the Chicago Park Board, in desperation, to choose one of the least appropriate of all forms, the strictly modern Dano-Norwegian *Eriksen*.

Other names ending in *-son* have been treated accordingly when they occur in the old saga. Such a form as *Bjarni Herjulfson* is therefore to be understood as a shortcut for " Bjarni, Herjulf's son," which might have been a better English rendition except for its awkwardness. The old Norsemen regularly identified themselves as sons of their fathers, a practice which still flourishes in Iceland.

A great many placenames and nicknames consist of elements whose meaning is completely clear to any Scandinavian, but which are merely a jumble of meaningless letters to an American. Whenever such names could easily be translated into a similar English form which would give them some of the vividness in English that they have in Icelandic, this was done. Instead of *Øxna-Thori* we have written " Ox-Thori," for *Furðustrandir* " Wonderstrands," for *Haukdalir* " Hawkdale," and for *Breiða-fjǫrðr* " Broadfjord." This we have not done for *Vinland*,

Markland, and *Helluland,* because these are well-established in English and not difficult to remember. Names which would sound awkward in English translation were usually left in a form approximating that of the Icelandic: Brattahlid, Sudrey, Hraunhofn. One name has been deliberately changed in spelling to avoid a common mispronunciation: " Karlsevni " instead of *Karlsefni.*

The poems which appear in the text are of an exceedingly intricate metrical form which could not possibly be rendered into comprehensible English, and any English versification that might be adopted would sound false. Hence the poetry has simply been rendered into rhythmic prose and set up in lines like those of the original.

In all aspects of translation our principle has been one: to produce an accurate and readable version of the ancient saga, by drawing upon the labors of specialists for the pleasure and benefit of interested amateurs. With this brief apologia we are happy to present: *The Saga of Vinland.*

CONTENTS

SECTION I. The Saga of Vinland

SECTION II. The Evidence of History —

A Commentary on the Saga of Vinland

ILLUSTRATIONS

SECTION I

THE SAGA OF VINLAND

Chapter I

ERIC THE RED SETTLES

IN GREENLAND

At Jadar in Norway there lived a man named Thorvald, who was the son of Osvald, the son of Ulf, the son of Ox-Thori. He had a son named Eric the Red. Father and son fled from Norway on account of a killing, and took land at Hornstrands in Iceland, on a place called Drangar. By this time Iceland was well settled. After Thorvald's death, Eric was married to Thjodhild, a daughter of Jorund Ulfson and Thorbjorg the Shipbreasted, whose second husband was Thorbjorn of Hawkdale. After his marriage Eric moved away from the north of Iceland, cleared land in Hawkdale, and settled at Ericsstead near Waterhorn.

Then Eric's slaves caused a landslide to crash down on Valthjof's Stead, a farm owned by one Valthjof. Eyolf the Filthy, a relative of Valthjof's, killed the slaves at a place not far from Waterhorn. For this Eric killed Eyolf and a man named Raven the Fighter. He was prosecuted by Eyolf's relatives, Geirstein and Odd at Jorvi, and they got him banished from Hawkdale.

Eric then seized Brokey and Oxney, two islands in the mouth of the fjord, and lived the first winter at Tradar on

Sudrey. Here he lent his neighbor Thorgest some hall beams [the end pieces of a raised dais along the sides of the hall]. Later he moved to Oxney, where he built a farm and called it Ericsstead. He asked to get his hall beams back, but was refused, and so he went to fetch them himself at Breidabolstead. Thorgest pursued him, and they fought near the farm of Drangar. Two of Thorgest's sons fell there, and some other men besides. After this both Eric and his enemies kept their farms well-manned. Eric was backed by Styr, by Eyolf from Sviney, the sons of Thorbrand of Swandale, and Thorbjorn Vifilson. Thorgest's backing came from the sons of Thord the Yeller, Thorgeir of Hitterdale, Aslak of Longdale, and his son Illugi.

The case came up at the Thorsness Thing session, and the Saga of the Ere-Dwellers tells us that there was a huge crowd. Styr was Eric's special helper in court, and did what he could to draw men away from Thorgest. He begged Snorri the Chief not to help Thorgest's men pursue Eric after the session. For this he promised to help Snorri some other time, if Snorri should ever be in trouble. Eric had his ship ready to sail in Eric's Bay. The court outlawed him, but his friend Eyolf hid him in Dimun's Bay, while Thorgest's men were out with many ships hunting for him among the islands.

Thorbjorn and Eyolf and Styr accompanied him out beyond the islands, and there they said goodbye to him with the greatest of friendliness. Eric assured them that he would repay what they had done for him, if it lay within his power, and if they should ever need it. He told his friends that he planned to go in search of that country which Gunnbjorn, son of Ulf the Crow, had sighted when he blew out of his course to the west of Iceland. Gunnbjorn had seen some rocks, and they were known as

Gunnbjorn's Reefs. Eric declared that if he found this country, he would come back and tell his friends about it.

Eric sailed from Snowfell-Glacier, and first sighted Greenland at Mid-Glacier, where there is a peak known as Black-sark. Then he sailed southwards along the coast, trying to find a livable spot, until he rounded the southern tip. He spent the first winter at Eric's Island, midway in what was later called the Eastern Settlement. The following spring he made his way to Ericsfjord and there took land for himself. That summer he spent much time exploring the uninhabited lands to the west, and wherever he went, he gave names to the tracts he visited. The second winter he lived at Eric's Holm off Hvarfsgnipa, near the southern tip of Greenland. The third summer he went as far north as Snowfell and entered Ravensfjord. He said that he got as far as the head of Ericsfjord before he turned back and spent the third winter on Eric's Island at the mouth of the fjord.

A D
982

The next summer he returned to Iceland, where he landed in Broadfjord, and spent the winter with Ingolf at Holmlatr. In the spring he fought once more with Thorgest, but was beaten. After that a truce was patched up between them. That summer Eric sailed away to colonize the country he had found. He called it Greenland, because — as he put it — people would be more anxious to go there if it had an attractive name. He told people that it was admirably suited for settling, and that it was richly endowed with nature's gifts: there was a great plenty of game — including seals, whales, walruses, bears, and other animals. In this way he tried to persuade people to settle in the new country.

A D
986

Eric made his home at Brattahlid [Steep-slope] in Ericsfjord. It is said by learned men that twenty-five ships sailed from Broadfjord and Borgfjord in Iceland during the

summer that Eric settled in Greenland. But only fourteen
of these ever reached Greenland, for some were driven
back, and others were wrecked. That was fourteen [or
fifteen] years before Christianity was made the law in
Iceland.

Chapter II

FROM THE GREENLAND SAGA

BJARNI HERJULFSON GLIMPSES
UNKNOWN SHORES

Herjulf was a son of Bard, the son of Herjulf. He was related to that Ingolf who was the first settler in Iceland, and who had given Herjulf's people land between Vog and Reykjaness. Herjulf lived at Drepstock with his wife Thorgerd and a son named Bjarni. This Bjarni was a talented fellow and from early youth his thoughts had turned to the sea. His trading voyages won him wealth and honor; before long he mastered a ship of his own. He made it his custom to live with his father in Iceland one winter and sail abroad the next.

During the last winter that Bjarni was in Norway, his father Herjulf broke up their home in Iceland and prepared to leave for Greenland with Eric the Red. Aboard Herjulf's ship there was a Christian man from the Hebrides, and he made a poem on the trip that was known as " The Song of the Breakers." One verse ran as follows:

> I pray our Christ will bless this voyage,
> The faultless One, who tests His servants;
> He rules the vaulted halls of heaven;
> May He extend His hand o'er us!

Herjulf settled at Herjulfsness and was held in the greatest respect.

That summer Bjarni sailed to Eyrar in Iceland only to
find that his father had left in the spring. This news
affected Bjarni a good deal, and he would not even trouble
to unload his ship. His men asked him what he had in
mind, and he answered that he planned to spend the winter with his father as he had always done — " and if you
will go with me, I shall steer straight for Greenland."
They all agreed to do as he thought best.

Then Bjarni said, " People will call us fools for start-
ing off on this voyage — we who have never been in the
Greenland seas! "

A D
986

In spite of this, they put to sea as soon as they could get
ready and sailed for three days. There was then no land in
sight, the fair wind died down, and they were beset by fogs
and north winds until they lost all track of their course.
This went on for many days, and then the sun came out
again, so they could get their bearings. They hoisted sail
and sailed all day before they sighted land. They won-
dered what country this might be, but it was Bjarni's opinion that it could not be Greenland. They asked him, was
he going to land, but he said, " It is my advice that we only
skirt the shore." As they did so, they found that the land
was not mountainous but covered with small wooded
knolls.

They left the land behind on their port side, with the
sheet pointed towards the shore. They sailed for two days
and found another country. They asked Bjarni if he
thought that this would be Greenland, but he replied that
this was no more Greenland than the other one, " for in
Greenland there are said to be huge glaciers." As they
approached the shore, they saw that it was a level country
and well wooded. The wind died down and the crew in-

BJARNI HERJULFSON SIGHTS NEW

LANDS IN THE WEST

sisted that they ought to land, but Bjarni refused. The men claimed that they were short of wood and water. "You have no lack of either," said Bjarni, but at this the men grumbled a good deal. He told them to hoist sail, and then they steered the ship away from shore.

For three days they sailed with a southwesterly breeze before they caught sight of a third coast. This country had many high mountains topped with glaciers. Again they asked Bjarni if he was going to land, and again he said no, "for this country looks pretty worthless to me." This time they did not even furl their sail but steered along the coast and found that it was an island. Again they left the country astern and sailed away in the same direction. A storm blew up and Bjarni told his crew to reef the sail and not to press on any faster than their ship and her tackle could bear.

They sailed for four days and then they found a fourth country. Again they asked Bjarni if he thought this was Greenland, and Bjarni answered, "This is most like what I have been told about Greenland, and here we shall try to land." So that evening they made their way to a jutting headland. On the cape they found a boat, and it was the very cape on which Herjulf, Bjarni's father, had settled and to which he had given his name, so that it has since been known as Herjulfsness. Bjarni now went to his father's house and from this time on he sailed no more. He lived with his father as long as Herjulf was alive, and after that he succeeded him and went on living there. But people found fault with him for showing so little curiosity and bringing back so little information about the countries he had visited.

Chapter III

FROM THE KARLSEVNI SAGA

LEIF ERICSON AT KING OLAF'S COURT

Eric the Red lived at Brattahlid, where he was held in the highest respect and deferred to by all. Eric's children were Leif, Thorvald, Thorstein, and a daughter named Freydis. She was married to one Thorvard and lived with him at Gardar, which is now the Bishop's seat. She was a proud and grasping woman, but Thorvard was a weakling. Thorstein lived at home with his father, and there was no more promising youth in all Greenland. In those days the people of Greenland were still pagan.

A D
999

One summer Eric's son Leif sailed for Norway to visit the court of King Olaf Trygvason. On his way from Greenland he was blown out of his course and landed on the Hebrides, off the west coast of Scotland. The winds kept blowing contrary for a long time, and he had to stay there most of the summer. Here Leif grew fond of a woman named Thorgunna. She was of good family, and, as Leif discovered, not without some knowledge of secret lore. When Leif was making ready to sail, Thorgunna begged to be taken along. Leif asked if this would be agreeable to her family, but she said that made no difference. Leif, however, refused to carry off a woman of her high rank in a strange country where, as he said, " we are so few in number."

" Some day," said Thorgunna, " you may regret that you chose this course."

" I shall have to risk that," retorted Leif.

" Then I will tell you," said Thorgunna, " that I am no longer alone; I am with child, and I say that it is your doing. I also know that I shall bear a boy when the time comes. And even though you pay no attention to me now, I shall bring him up and send him to you in Greenland, as soon as he can travel with other men. But I predict that he will give you no more joy than you deserve from this parting with me. More than that, I intend to see Greenland myself before the end comes."

When he left, Leif gave her a gold ring, a homespun Greenland mantle, and a belt of walrus-tusk. Later on, the boy did come to Greenland, and he was named Thorgils. Leif accepted him as his son, and after that the boy stayed in Greenland, but to the very end there was something uncanny about him.

Leif now sailed away from the Hebrides and got to Norway by fall. He sought the court of King Olaf Trygvason, and entered his service. The king showed Leif great favor, for it seemed to him that Leif was a fine, well-bred man.

One time he called Leif in and asked him, " Are you planning to sail out to Greenland this summer? "

" I am," answered Leif, " if it is not against your will."

" Indeed," said the king, " I am anxious that you should. You shall go with a special mission from me: to proclaim Christianity in Greenland." Leif said he would do as the king wished, but added that it might not be an easy mission to accomplish in Greenland. The king insisted, however, that he knew no man better fitted for it than Leif.

" And I am confident," he added, " that fortune will
smile on you."

" That will only be," said Leif, " if your good luck is
added to mine."

Leif sailed as soon as he could get ready, and was blown
around a great deal. He hit upon countries he had not expected to see. There he found self-sown wheat fields and
grapevines, and a tree called " mosur " [possibly bird's-
eye maple], and he brought with him samples of all these.
Some of the timber was big enough to use in building
houses. Leif found some shipwrecked men and took them
home with him and gave them all lodgings for the winter.
He showed so noble and generous a nature — in bringing
Christianity to Greenland and in rescuing these men —
that after this he was called Leif the Lucky.

Leif landed in Ericsfjord and made his way home to
Brattahlid, where he was well received. He set out at once
to preach Christianity and the Catholic faith. He showed
men the tokens of King Olaf's mission and told them how
much glory and magnificence followed this faith. Eric was
very reluctant about giving up his old beliefs. But his wife
Thjodhild quickly went over to Christianity and had a
church built some distance from their home. The church
was named Thjodhild's church after her. There she used
to say her prayers, along with all the rest who accepted the
faith, and they were many. Thjodhild refused to have in-
tercourse with Eric after she was converted, and this he
took greatly to heart.

Eric grumbled that the one of Leif's deeds offset the
other: he had rescued a ship's crew and saved their lives;
but he had also brought this " faker " to Greenland —
that was his name for the priest. Yet Leif's urging and persuasion brought about the baptism of Eric and all the
people of Greenland.

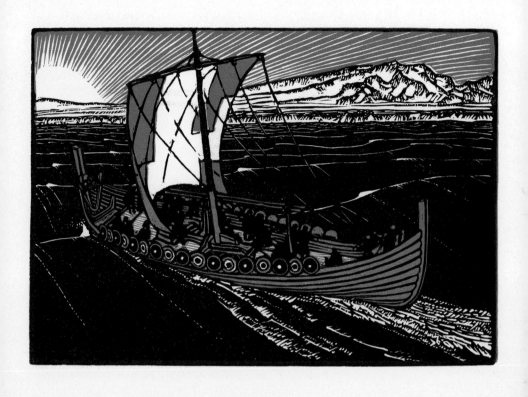

LEIF ERICSON SAILS OFF TO EXPLORE THE

LANDS SEEN BY BJARNI

Chapter IV

LEIF ERICSON EXPLORES VINLAND

People in Greenland were now eagerly talking about exploring the lands that had been seen. Leif Ericson made a visit to Bjarni Herjulfson and bought a ship from him. Then he gathered a crew of thirty-five men and asked his father Eric to lead the expedition. But Eric held back. " I am getting along in years," he said, " and I am less able to put up with such hardships than I used to be."

But Leif insisted that he was still the ablest and the luckiest of his clan, and gradually he talked Eric into consenting. When they were ready, Eric rode from home, and got almost down to the ship. Then the horse he was riding stumbled, so he fell off and hurt his foot. Eric then said, " It seems that I am not fated to find other lands than the one in which we are now living. We shall ride no farther together." Eric returned to Brattahlid, while Leif went down to the ship with his thirty-five companions. One of them was a German by the name of Tyrker.

They fitted out the ship and sailed away. The first country they found was the one that Bjarni had seen last. Here they sailed to shore and dropped anchor, put out a boat and went on land. They saw no grass, the mountain tops

A D
1002

were covered with glaciers, and from sea to mountain the country was like one slab of rock. It looked to be a barren, unprofitable country. Then Leif remarked, "Now at least we have done better than Bjarni, who never even set foot on these shores! I am going to give the country a name, and I shall call it Helluland [the land of flat rocks]."

They went on board and sailed out to sea once more. They found a second country, and again they dropped anchor, put out a boat, and went ashore. This country was level and wooded, with broad white beaches wherever they went, and a gently sloping shoreline. Leif said, " I shall give this country a name that fits with its natural character and call it Markland [forest land]." Then they hurried back to their ships and sailed on with a northeast breeze.

After two days' sail they sighted another shore and landed on an island to the north of the mainland. It was a fine, bright day, and as they looked around, they discovered dew on the grass. It so happened that they picked up some of the dew in their hands and tasted of it, and it seemed to them that they had never tasted anything so sweet. Then they returned to the ship and sailed through the channel between the island and a cape jutting out to the north of the mainland.

They steered a westerly course past the cape and found great shallows at ebb tide, so that their ship was beached and lay some distance from the sea. But they were so eager to go ashore that they could not bear to wait till the tide rose under their ship. They ran up on the shore to a place where a stream flowed out of a lake. As soon as the sea rose under their ship, they took a boat and rowed out to it, and moved it up the river into the lake, where they cast anchor. Then they took their leather hammocks ashore and built themselves shelters. Later they decided

ERIC THE RED FALLS FROM

HIS HORSE

to stay there through the winter and set up large houses.

There was no lack of salmon either in the river or in the lake, and it was bigger salmon than they had ever seen. Nature was so generous here that it seemed to them no cattle would need any winter fodder, but could graze outdoors. There was no frost in winter, and the grass hardly withered. The days and nights were more nearly equal than in Greenland or Iceland, and on the shortest day of the year the sun was up from breakfast time to midafternoon [as it was not in Iceland after the middle of October].

When they had finished building their houses, Leif said to his companions, " Now I am going to divide our company into two groups, for I want to get this country explored. Half the men will stay here at the camp, while the other half goes exploring. They shall not go so far that they cannot get back home by evening, and they shall stay together." So for a time they did this, and sometimes Leif went along with the exploring party and sometimes he stayed at home. Leif was a big, strapping fellow, handsome to look at, thoughtful and temperate in all things.

One evening the news spread that a member of the crew was missing, none other than Tyrker the German. Leif was much disturbed at this, for Tyrker had lived in their household a long time and had been greatly devoted to Leif when he was a child. Leif angrily reproached his men, and made ready to start off with a search party of twelve. They had scarcely left the house when Tyrker came walking towards them, and he was received with great joy. Leif saw at once that his foster father was in high spirits. Tyrker was a short fellow, rather puny looking, with a prominent forehead and restless eyes in a smallish face; but he was handy at all sorts of craftsmanship.

Leif said to him, " Why were you so late, foster father,

and how did you get parted from your company? " Tyrker first talked a long time in German, rolled his eyes and made faces. They did not understand a word he said. After a while he changed over and spoke Norse.

" I did not go very far beyond the rest of you, and yet I have some real news for you. I found grape vines and grapes! "

" Is this really true, foster father mine? " said Leif.

" Certainly it is true," he answered, " for I was born where there is no lack either of vines or grapes."

Now they slept that night, but the next morning Leif told his crew, " From now on we have two jobs on our hands. On one day we shall gather grapes, and on the next we shall cut grape vines and chop down the trees to make a cargo for my ship."

So they followed this plan, and it is said that they loaded up the afterboat with grapes, and the ship itself with a cargo of timber. When spring came, they made the ship ready and sailed away. Leif gave this country a name to suit its resources: he called it Vinland [wine land].

After this they sailed out to sea with favorable winds, until they hove in sight of Greenland and its ice-capped mountains. Then one of the crew spoke up and asked Leif, " Why do you steer the ship so much into the wind? "

" I am watching the course," answered Leif, " but I can also see something else. Do *you* notice anything out of the ordinary? " They answered that they saw nothing worth talking about.

" I wonder," said Leif, " if the thing I see is a ship or a reef."

Then they saw it, and said that it must be a reef. But Leif's eyes were so much keener than theirs that he could see men on the reef.

" Now," said Leif, " we shall steer into the wind, so that

TYRKER THE GERMAN

FINDS GRAPES

we can help these men if they need it. If they should happen to be unfriendly, we have the upper hand and not they."

They sailed in by the reef, lowered their sail, cast anchor, and launched a little boat they had with them. Tyrker asked the men, " Who is your chief? " One of them spoke up, " My name is Thori, and I am of Norse stock. But what is your name? "

Leif told him.

" Are you the son of Eric the Red of Brattahlid? " said he.

" I am," said Leif, " and now I wish to invite you all on board my ship, and you may take as much of your goods as the ship will hold."

They accepted his offer and sailed with their cargo to Ericsfjord. They landed at Brattahlid, and here they unloaded the ship. Leif asked Thori and his wife Gudrid and three of the men to make their home with him, and he found lodgings elsewhere for the rest of the crew, both Thori's men and his own. Leif rescued fifteen persons from the reef.

So Leif grew in wealth and honor. But that winter there was much sickness among Thori's men, and Thori himself died, together with a large part of his crew.

Chapter V

THORVALD ERICSON GOES

EXPLORING

People kept talking a great deal about Leif's voyage to Vinland, and his brother Thorvald maintained that the country was still too scantily explored. Leif spoke to him and said, " If you are burning to see Vinland, brother, you are welcome to my ship. But first I should like to send the ship to fetch the timber that Thori had on the reef." This was done.

A D
1004

Then Thorvald got ready for the voyage with a crew of thirty men, consulting all the time with his brother Leif. They fixed up the ship and sailed away, and nothing is reported to have happened before they got to Vinland. At Leif's camp they laid up their ship and spent the winter, getting their food by fishing.

A D
1005

In the spring Thorvald told his men to get the ship ready. He sent some of them out with the afterboat and asked them to spend the summer exploring the coast to the west. They found that it was a lovely, wooded country, and that the woods ran almost down to the sea, with a white, sandy beach. The sea was full of islands and great shallows. Nowhere did they find any vestiges of men or animals, except a wooden granary on one of the islands to

LEIF RESCUES FIFTEEN PERSONS FROM A REEF

the west. They found no other human product, and in the fall they turned back to Leif's camp.

In the second summer Thorvald sailed his vessel eastward and along the coast to the north. As they were rounding a certain cape, a stiff storm fell upon them and drove them on shore, so that their keel was broken and they had to stay there a long time while they repaired the ship. Then Thorvald said to his men, " I wish we might raise up the keel on this cape and call the cape Keelness," and so they did.

A D
1006

Then they sailed along the coast to the east, into some nearby fjord mouths, and headed for a jutting cape that rose high out of the sea and was all covered with woods. Here they anchored the ship and laid down a gangplank to the shore. Thorvald went ashore with all his company. Then he said, " This is beautiful, and here I should like to build me a home."

After a time they went back to the ship. Then they caught sight of three little mounds on the sand farther in on the cape. When they got closer to them, they saw three skin-covered boats, with three men under each. They split up their force and seized all the men but one, who escaped in his boat. They killed all eight of them, and then returned to the cape. Here they saw a number of mounds in the fjord and guessed that these must be human dwelling places.

After that such a drowsiness fell upon them that they simply could not stay awake, and they all fell asleep. Then a voice cried out to them, so that they all awoke, and this is what the voice said, " Wake up, Thorvald, and all your crew, if you value your lives! Get aboard the ship with your men and hurry away from this country with all speed! " A host of boats was then heading towards them from the inner end of the fjord. Thorvald then said, " We shall set up our breastworks on both sides of the ship and defend ourselves as best we can, but do as little killing as possible." So they did, and after the savages had shot at them for a while, they hurried away as fast as they could.

Thorvald asked if any of his men were wounded. They said they were not.

" I have got a wound under my arm," he said; " an arrow flew between the gunwale and my shield and struck me under the arm, and here is the arrow. This will be the last of me. Now I advise you to make ready for your return as quickly as possible. But me you shall take back to that cape which I found so inviting. It looks as if I spoke the truth without knowing it when I said that I might live there some day! Bury me there with a cross at my head and another at my feet, and ever after you shall call it Crossness."

So Thorvald died and they did everything just as he had told them. Then they came back to their companions and exchanged news about all that had happened. They spent the winter there and gathered grapes and vines for the ship. The next spring they sailed back to Greenland and steered the ship into Ericsfjord and had plenty of news to tell Leif.

A D
1007

DEATH OF THORVALD ERICSON

Chapter VI

THORBJORN AND GUDRID
EMIGRATE

Thorbjorn was the name of an Icelandic chief, who had a great estate and was held in the highest honor. He had a daughter named Gudrid, who was the loveliest of women and noble in every trait.

A man named Orm, who lived at Arnarstapi and was married to Halldis, was a great friend of Thorbjorn's. He was an excellent farmer, and for a long time Gudrid was brought up in his household.

There was a rich man named Thorgeir, who once had been a slave, and now lived at Thorgeir's Fell. He had a son Einar, who was a handsome, manly fellow, and quite fond of showy clothes. Einar used to sail on trading expeditions and prospered in this business; he spent his winters alternately in Iceland and Norway. One fall Einar was selling off a cargo of his on Snowfellsness in Iceland and came to Orm's home at Arnarstapi. Orm invited him to stay there, and Einar accepted, for they were good friends. Einar's wares were carried into one of the storehouses, and there Einar unpacked them and showed them to Orm and his household.

He offered Orm anything he wanted, and Orm ac-

cepted, saying that Einar was a fine merchant and a man
of good fortune.

Just as they were busy with the wares, a woman walked
past the storehouse door. Einar asked Orm who the beautiful woman was that had walked past the door — " I have
never seen her here before."

" That," replied Orm, " is Gudrid, my foster child; she
is a daughter of Thorbjorn, the chief of Laugarbrekka."

" She would be a fine match for me," said Einar. " Or
has she already been spoken for? "

" Plenty of men have asked for her, my friend," answered Orm, " but she is not to be had for the asking. It
looks as if both she and her father were pretty particular."

" Be that as it may," said Einar, " she is the woman I
intend to ask for, and I wish that you would plead my
cause with her father. If you will go to this trouble for
my sake, I shall reward you with my devoted friendship.
Thorbjorn will surely see the advantage in tying up with
us; for he has a high standing and a fine estate, but they
tell me that his other assets are slipping away. Now my
father and I have plenty of land and goods, and it would
be a great help to Thorbjorn if he would accept this plan."

" I certainly consider myself a friend of yours," replied
Orm, " but I do not look forward to broaching this idea to
Thorbjorn — he is a proud man and a hot-tempered one,
too."

But Einar insisted that he make the proposal, and at
length Orm agreed to do as he wished. Then Einar went
back south to his home.

Some time after this, Thorbjorn held a great harvest
festival, as was his custom, for he was a princely sort of
man. Orm of Arnarstapi was asked there, along with many
other friends of Thorbjorn's. Orm got to talking with
Thorbjorn and told him that he had lately been visited

THE BURIAL OF THORVALD AT CROSSNESS

by Einar of Thorgeir's Fell and that Einar was a promising young man. He then made the proposal on Einar's behalf and said that there were many reasons why he should accept the offer. " It would help you out of your difficulties."

Thorbjorn answered, " I had not expected to hear such words from you, that I should marry my daughter to the son of a slave. Now that you think my wealth is waning, you can give me such advice as this. But she shall no longer stay with you, who have found her worthy of so mean a marriage."

Orm and the other guests went back to their homes. But that winter Gudrid stayed at home with her father. In the spring Thorbjorn again gave a grand feast for his friends; many people came, and it was a great party. One day at the feast Thorbjorn asked them to listen, and then he spoke these words: " I have lived here a whole lifetime; I have many proofs of the love and good will of men towards me, and it seems to me that our dealings have been good. But now things are taking a turn for the worse, because my fortune is running low, though people have never scorned me before. Now I will rather break up my home than blemish my honor; I will rather leave the country than disgrace my family. So I have decided to accept the proposal that my friend Eric the Red made when we parted in Broadfjord. I plan to leave for Greenland this summer, if things go as I wish."

This speech caused a great sensation, for Thorbjorn had many friends; but they realized that he had only announced the plan when his mind was fully made up, and that there was no use in trying to change it. Thorbjorn gave gifts to his guests, and soon the party broke up, with the men returning to their homes.

Thorbjorn sold his land and bought a ship that was

lying at the mouth of Hraunhofn [Lava Harbor]. Thirty men made ready to sail with him, and among them Orm of Arnarstapi and his wife, as well as others of Thorbjorn's friends who did not wish to part from him. So they put out to sea, and at first the weather favored them. But on the high seas the good winds died down, a fearful storm broke upon them, and they were tossed around all summer. Besides, many of them fell sick, and half the company died, including Orm and his wife Halldis. The seas were rough, and the men had to bear all sorts of misery and distress. In spite of this they managed to make Herjulfsness in Greenland by the opening of winter [October 14]. A man named Thorkel was living on Herjulfsness at this time, a fine, enterprising farmer. He received Thorbjorn and all his men and entertained them royally throughout the winter. Thorbjorn and his men enjoyed themselves here and were well satisfied.

Chapter VII

GUDRID AND THE WITCH

It so happened that this was a bad year in Greenland, for the men who had gone fishing had made a poor haul and some had not even returned. There was a woman in the settlement named Thorbjorg, who was a fortune teller and was called the Little Witch. She had had nine sisters, all of them wise women, and she alone was alive. It was her custom to visit around among the farmers, and people invited her to their homes, especially those who were eager to know what the future had in store for them or what the season would be like. Since Thorkel was the leading man in this community, people felt that it was his duty to find out when their troubles were going to let up. Thorkel invited the witch woman to his home and prepared a fine welcome for her, as was the custom when such women were received. A special seat of honor was made ready for her, and a cushion laid in it, filled with chicken feathers.

A man was sent to fetch her. When he brought her back that evening, she was dressed in a dark-blue mantle, clasped together with a strap, and set with precious stones all the way down to the hem. She wore a necklace of glass beads, and on her head a black lambskin hood, lined with white catskin. She carried a staff with a knob on top, orna-

mented with brass and set with stones on top of the knob.
Around her waist she wore a belt made of tinderwood,
with a large leather bag hanging from it. In this bag she
kept the charms that she needed for her witchcraft. On
her feet she wore shaggy calfskin shoes, and the laces
were long, heavy leather thongs with big brass buttons on
the ends. On her hands she wore catskin gloves, which
were white and furry on the inside.

When she came in, everyone felt that it was proper to
greet her as courteously as possible, and she responded to
each as she found them agreeable to her. Thorkel, as head
of the house, took the witch woman by the hand and led
her to the seat that had been prepared for her. Then he
asked her to cast her eyes over home and herd and household; but she was very silent about it all.

In the evening tables were set up, and something must
be said about the meal that was prepared for the witch
woman. A porridge of goat's milk was made for her, and
she was served meat from the hearts of every kind of animal they had there. She used a brass spoon and a knife
with a handle of walrus tusk that was fastened on by a
double ring of copper; the point of it was broken. When
the tables were taken away, Thorkel went before Thorbjorg and asked her how she liked the household and the
behavior of the people, and how soon she would be able
to tell him what he had asked about and everyone wanted
to know. She said that she could give no answer before
morning, after she had slept there that night.

The next day they began to make the necessary prepa-
rations for carrying on her witchcraft. She asked to have
with her some women who knew the old magic song called
Warlocks, which was needed for the ritual. But there
seemed to be no such women. They hunted around the
farm, to see if any one knew it, and then Gudrid spoke

GUDRID SINGS THE MAGIC SONGS FOR

THORBJORG THE WITCH

up, " I am no witch woman, nor am I skilled in any kind of witchcraft, but Halldis my foster mother in Iceland taught me the lore that she called Warlocks."

Thorkel answered, " You are lucky to have learned it! "

" But this," said Gudrid, " is secret lore of a kind that I will have no part in, for I am a Christian woman."

" By giving us your help," said Thorbjorg, " you might very well do the people hereabouts a great service and yet be none the worse for it. But I trust that Thorkel will be able to persuade you."

Thorkel urged Gudrid to consent, and she finally agreed to do as he wished. The women then formed a circle around Thorbjorg, who sat on the magic platform. Gudrid recited the charm so well and so beautifully that none of them could remember having heard it done with finer expression. The witch woman thanked her for the song and said that many spirits had been attracted to the place and had been charmed by her recital, spirits who before had turned away and refused to show submission. " Now," she said, " many things are clear as daylight, which before were hidden both to me and others. For one thing, I know now that this bad season will only last the winter, and that things will get better in the spring. The pest that has been harassing you will vanish sooner than you expect. And as for you, Gudrid, I am going to reward you at once for the help you have given us, for your future lies clear before me. You will make a distinguished match here in Greenland, though the marriage will not be a long-lasting one, for your paths lead back to Iceland, and there you will become the mother of a great and good line and over your family tree will shine a brighter ray of light than I have the power to tell you. But now I bid you farewell and good luck, my daughter."

After this, people crowded around the witch woman

and each one asked about the things he most wanted to know. She was ready and willing to answer them, and not much of what she told them failed to come true. The people on another farm had already sent for her, and so she went there. Then they sent for Thorbjorn to return, for he had refused to stay home while such heathendom was being practised.

As soon as spring came, the weather got better, as Thorbjorg had said it would. Thorbjorn got his ship ready and sailed to Brattahlid. Eric received him with open arms and said it was well that he had come. Thorbjorn and his household lived with Eric that winter, while his crew lodged with the neighbors. The next spring Eric gave him land at Stockness, where Thorbjorn built himself a goodly farm and lived forever after.

A D
I000

Chapter VIII

FROM THE KARLSEVNI SAGA AND
THE GREENLAND SAGA

THORSTEIN ERICSON LOOKS

FOR VINLAND

Next it is to be told that Thorstein Ericson asked for the
hand of Gudrid, Thorbjorn's daughter. He was a good
man, wise and friendly, and his proposal was well received, both by Gudrid and her father Thorbjorn. It was
decided that they should be married, and the wedding was
arranged at Brattahlid in the fall. It was a great festival
and there were many guests. Gudrid was a fine-looking,
intelligent woman, with a gracious manner toward
strangers.

A D
1007

Thorstein was eager to explore the lands that his brother
Leif had found; according to the Greenland Saga, he also
wanted to bring back the body of his brother Thorvald.
He rigged up the ship that Thorvald had sailed in and
picked out a crew that was notable for strength and stature. With twenty-five men and Gudrid his wife he set
sail as soon as they were ready. But they were tossed around
all summer and never found the course they were looking
for. They got within sight of Iceland, and they saw birds
from the Irish coast. In the fall they got back to Greenland, weary and battered, reaching Ericsfjord just a week
before the beginning of winter.

A D
1008

Then Eric spoke these words, " You were more cheer
ful this summer, when you sailed out of the fjord, than
you are now; and yet things might be much worse! "
Thorstein replied, " You will show your true princely
spirit now, if you look after the homeless members of my
crew and see that they are well taken care of." So all those
who had no place to go went home to Eric's farm.

Thorstein owned a half share in a farm in Lysufjord,
the southernmost fjord of the Western Settlement. The
other half was owned by a man who also was named Thorstein, and often called " the Black "; his wife's name was
Sigrid. Thorstein and Gudrid made a visit to these people in Lysufjord. They were given a good welcome and
stayed there that winter.

Early in the winter a disease began to ravage Thorstein
Ericson's crew, and many of his men died. Thorstein
asked that coffins be made for those who died, and the
bodies brought aboard his ship. " For I intend," he said,
" to have all the dead removed to Ericsfjord next summer."

But it was not long before the plague struck Thorstein's
own household. First Sigrid, mistress of the house, fell
sick; she was a very big woman and as powerful as a man,
but the plague struck her down just the same. Shortly
after that the disease seized Thorstein Ericson, so that
they both lay sick at the same time. When Sigrid died,
Thorstein got up and went out of the house to find a
plank to lay the body on. Gudrid then said, " Don't stay
away long, Thorstein mine." He said he would not. Then
Thorstein exclaimed, " Our hostess is carrying on most
strangely, for she is trying to get up on her elbow and is
sticking her foot over the edge of the bed and fumbling
for her shoes."

Just then the other Thorstein came in, and Sigrid lay
down with a crash so that every beam in the house shook.

Now Thorstein made a coffin for Sigrid's body, took it away, and buried it. He was a big man and a strong one, but it took all the strength he had to get her off the farm.

Now Thorstein Ericson's illness got worse, and he died, to the great distress of his wife Gudrid. They were all sitting together in the room, with Gudrid on a chair before the bench where her husband was lying. Then the other Thorstein lifted Gudrid off the chair on to his lap and sat down with her on a bench opposite her dead husband. He spoke gently with her and tried to comfort her; he promised her that he would take her to Ericsfjord with her husband's body and those of his companions. " Also," he said, " I shall bring more servants here to wait on you and amuse you." She thanked him for this.

Thorstein Ericson sat up and cried, " Where is Gudrid? " He said it three times, but she did not answer. Then she asked the other Thorstein, " Shall I answer him or not? " He told her to say nothing. Then he walked across the floor to the chair and sat down on it, again taking Gudrid on his lap. Then he said to the dead man, " What do you want, namesake? "

After a pause Thorstein Ericson replied, " I feel an urge to tell Gudrid her coming fate, so that she will not take my death too hard, for I have come to a good resting place." He then went on to foretell those events which are recounted in the rest of this saga. He was seen to drop a tear and whisper some words in Gudrid's ear that only she could hear. Then he said aloud that those men were blessed who kept their Christian faith, for with it went grace and comfort; but there were many who kept it badly.

" It is a shameful custom," said he, " which people have followed here in Greenland since they took over Christianity — that they bury men in unconsecrated ground with just a little singing over them. I want to be removed to the church along with those of my crew who have died." It had become the custom in Greenland to bury men on the farms where they died. They were put down in unconsecrated soil, with a pole thrust down as far as the breast of the corpse. When the clergy arrived, the pole was pulled up, and holy water poured down the opening. Then a service was sung over the dead, though it might be a long time after their burial.

Thorstein told Gudrid she could look forward to a bright future. He advised her not to marry a Greenlander. He asked her to give their property to the church or to the poor, and then he fell back a second time.

A D

1009

Thorstein the Black carried out all that he had promised Gudrid. He sold his land and his cattle in the spring and sailed with her and all his goods to Ericsfjord. The dead were buried in the churchyard. Gudrid went to live in Leif's household at Brattahlid, while Thorstein the Black got himself a farm in Ericsfjord and lived there the rest of his life, honored and respected by all.

THORSTEIN ERICSON FORETELLS THE FUTURE

OF GUDRID

Chapter IX

FROM THE KARLSEVNI SAGA

KARLSEVNI AND GUDRID
ARE MARRIED

There was a man named Thorfinn Karlsevni [the promising], a son of Thord Horsehead, who lived in the north of Iceland at Reyniness in Skagafjord. Karlsevni was a man of good stock and very well-to-do. His mother's name was Thorunn. He used to sail on trading voyages and was considered a successful merchant.

One summer he made his ship ready with the idea of sailing to Greenland. Snorri, a son of Thorbrand from Alptafjord, joined him, and together they had a crew of forty men. That same summer two other men, Bjarni Grimolfson from Broadfjord and Thorhall Gamlason from Eastfjord, also fitted out a ship to sail to Greenland with forty men on board.

Both ships sailed out to sea as soon as they were ready. We are not told how long they were at sea, but in the fall they both arrived in Ericsfjord. Eric and other settlers rode down to the ships to meet them, and at once began bartering for the goods they had brought. The skippers told Eric to help himself to all he wanted of the wares. Eric showed his generosity in turn by inviting all the men

to Brattahlid for the winter. The traders thanked Eric
for the offer and went home with him. Later their wares
were carried to Brattahlid, where there was no lack of fine,
roomy outhouses to store them in.

The traders had a merry time of it at Eric's place that
winter. But as it drew toward Christmas, Eric became
silent and moody, very different from his usual cheerful
self. One day Karlsevni got to talking with him and said,
"Are you troubled about something, Eric? It strikes us
that you are rather less cheerful than you have been. You
are treating us so royally here that we owe you whatever
returns we can give. Now tell me what makes you so
gloomy."

Eric replied, "You are fine, courteous guests, and nothing is farther from my thoughts than any unpleasantness
between us. It is simply that I should feel deeply shamed
if it came to be said that you had never had so bad a
Christmas as the one you spent at Eric the Red's in Greenland."

"There is no need of that," answered Karlsevni. "On
our ships we have malt and flour and grain, and you are
welcome to take as much as you wish, and hold whatever
kind of celebration your generosity may dictate."

Eric accepted the offer and made ready for the Christmas feast, and it turned out so magnificently that people
could hardly recall a better one in a poor country.

After Christmas Karlsevni asked Eric for Gudrid's
hand, since it appeared that Eric had the legal right to
marry her off. Eric answered that he would be glad to
advance his cause, and he added that she deserved to be
well married. "She will have to follow the fate that is cut
out for her, and we have heard nothing but good about
you." The question was then put up to her, and she said

that her wishes agreed wholly with Eric's. They wasted no time carrying out the plan, and extended the Christmas feast into a wedding party. It was a jolly winter in Brattahlid that year, with much chess-playing, saga-telling, and everything that might contribute to their good cheer.

Chapter X

KARLSEVNI LEADS AN EXPEDITION

There was great discussion at Brattahlid that winter about going in search of Vinland the Good, for it was agreed that the country must have valuable resources. For this reason Karlsevni and Snorri decided to go exploring in A D the spring. Bjarni and Thorhall, who were mentioned 1010 above, made ready to join them with their ship and the crew they had brought from Iceland.

There was a man named Thorvard, who was married to Freydis, an illegitimate daughter of Eric's. He also decided to go along. With him came Thorhall, who was nicknamed " The Hunter." He and Eric used to go hunting and fishing together in the summer, while in the winter he was Eric's overseer and trusted man. He was huge of stature, dark and glowering, rather beyond middle age; he was a hard man to get along with, mostly taciturn, but also abusive and underhanded, and he was a bad adviser to Eric. He had refused to adopt the new faith when it came to Greenland. He had few friends, but Eric had a high regard for him, and he was taken on the voyage because he was acquainted far and wide with the unsettled regions of the country. They sailed the ship that Thor-

THE SCOTTISH RUNNERS HAKI

AND HEKJA

bjorn, Gudrid's father, had brought out from Iceland, and most of the men aboard were Greenlanders.

Altogether there were a hundred and sixty men aboard the three ships. They sailed first to the Western Settlement and then out to Bear Isles. From there they sailed for two days with a northerly wind before they sighted land. They rowed to shore in their boats and explored the country; here they found huge slabs of stone, many of them twenty-four feet across [the Greenland Saga says that two men could easily lie outstretched on them with their soles touching]. They saw many arctic foxes there. They named the country Helluland [the land of flat rocks]. Then they sailed for two days more, with their course turning from south to southeast, and reached a land with great forests and many animals. Off the shore to the southeast lay an island, and here they killed a bear. For this reason they called it Bear Island, while they named the country itself Markland [forest land] because of the woods.

Then they sailed a long time along the coast and came upon a cape. They tacked along the coast, which was on their starboard. It was an unfriendly shoreline, with long, sandy beaches. They put out their boats and rowed ashore. On the cape they found the keel of a ship, and so they called it Keelness. The sandy beaches they called Wonderstrands, because it took so long to sail past them. Then the coast grew more indented with bays, and they steered the ship into one of these.

When Leif Ericson had been at the court of Olaf Trygvason, and King Olaf had asked him to proclaim Christianity in Greenland, he had given Leif two Scottish [Gaelic] people, a man named Haki and a woman named Hekja. The king suggested that if he needed speed, he might use them, for they were swifter than deer. Leif and Eric had turned them over to Karlsevni for the voyage.

When they had sailed past Wonderstrands, they landed the
Scots and told them to run southwards and see what the
country had to offer, but to return before three days were
past. They were dressed in garments which they called
" kjafal " [Irish *cabhail*]. These were made with a hood
on top, were open on the sides, sleeveless, and fastened
between the legs with a button and a loop. Otherwise the
Scots were naked.

They cast anchor and lay there in the meanwhile. When
three days had passed, the Scots came running down to the
shore. One of them bore a bunch of grapes in his hand,
the other an ear of wild wheat. Karlsevni declared that
they seemed to have found a country rich in resources, and
took them back on board. Then they all sailed away on
their course, until they reached a place where the shoreline was broken by a fjord, and into this fjord they headed
their ships. At the mouth lay an island, washed by swift
ocean currents; this they called Stream Isle. There were
so many eider-ducks there that it was hardly possible to
step between the eggs. They steered into the fjord and
called it Streamfjord.

Here they unloaded their cargoes and set up a camp.
They had brought along all kinds of livestock, and now
they turned them out to graze in the tall grass. There were
mountains there, and the country was beautiful to see. The
men spent all their time exploring. They stayed throughout the winter, which turned out to be a severe one. They
had not provided for it during the summer, and so they
ran short of food, and had trouble finding any game or
fish.

They went out to the island in the hope that something
would turn up — either wild life or flotsam from the sea.
But there was little that one could eat, even though their
cattle were getting along fine. Then they prayed to God,

FISH ARE CAUGHT IN PITS AT

HIGH TIDE

and asked that He send them some food, but their prayers were not answered as quickly as they had need of. Meanwhile Thorhall the Hunter disappeared and the men made a search for him, keeping it up for three days. On the fourth day Karlsevni and Bjarni found him on top of an overhanging cliff. He was staring up in the air, with his eyes and mouth and nostrils wide open, while he scratched and pinched himself, and mumbled something. They asked why he had gone there. He told them it was none of their business, that they had better not bother about his actions, and that he had lived long enough so he needed no advice from them.

They told him to come home with them, and he did so. Soon afterwards a whale drifted in, and the men rushed at it and cut it up, but they did not know what kind of whale this was. Even Karlsevni, who was an expert on whales, could not make out what kind it was. When the cooks had boiled the whalemeat, they ate some of it; but all of them got sick from it. Then Thorhall walked over and said to them, " Isn't it so that the Redbearded One turned out to be stronger than your Christ? This is my reward for the poetry I made about my trusty friend Thor; he has rarely failed me." When the men learned this, none of them would touch the meat, and they threw it over a cliff into the sea. They uplifted their voices and asked for the mercy of God. Then the weather got better, so they could row out to sea, and now they were able to find plenty of food. In the spring they went back to Streamfjord and gathered supplies along the shore. There was game on the mainland, birds' nests on the island, and fish in the sea.

Now they began to discuss the future course of their journey. Thorhall the Hunter wanted to sail north of Wonderstrands past Keelness and look for Vinland in this direction, while Karlsevni wanted to sail southward along

the coast and to the east of it, for there seemed to be better
land the farther south they got, and it seemed to him more
advisable to explore in both directions. Thorhall rigged
up his ship off the island, but only nine men went with
him. All the rest joined Karlsevni. One day, as Thorhall
was carrying water on board his ship, he took a drink and
recited this verse:

> Warrior friends so brave
> promised me so much;
> best of drinks I'd get
> in this repulsive land.
> Yet here you see me now,
> creeping to the spring,
> swinging a water pail;
> no wine has touched my lips.

After this they sailed away, and Karlsevni followed
them out to the island. Before they hoisted sail, Thorhall
recited another ditty:

> Let's be off for home,
> steer across the waves,
> cleave the ocean paths,
> back to our countrymen.
> Let the restless stay,
> all who praise this land;
> let them sit and cook
> their whales on Wonderstrand.

Then they parted company, and Thorhall and his crew
sailed to the north past Wonderstrands and Keelness.
There they tried to tack to the west, but a storm struck
them and blew them east as far as Ireland. Here they were
beaten up and thrown into slavery, and Thorhall lost his
life, according to stories told by traders.

Karlsevni sailed south along the coast with Snorri,

THE SKRAELINGS EXCHANGE FURS

FOR STRIPS OF CLOTH

Bjarni, and the rest. After a long while they came to a stream that first ran down into a lake, and then into the sea. There were great sandbars outside the river mouth, and they could only enter the stream at high tide. Karls-evni then sailed into the river mouth and named the country Hop, because that was the Norse word for a small, landlocked bay. Here they found self-sown wheat fields in the lowlands, and grapevines wherever there were hills. Every creek was full of fish. They dug pits at the point where land and sea met at high tide, and when the tide went out, there were halibut in the pits. The woods teemed with all kinds of animals. For half a month they stayed there and enjoyed themselves, without being aware of any dangers. They had their livestock with them.

Chapter XI

FROM THE KARLSEVNI SAGA

KARLSEVNI MEETS THE NATIVES

Early one morning, as they were looking around, they caught sight of a great many skin-covered boats. The men in the boats were waving wooden sticks at the ships, and they were waving them in a sunwise direction. It sounded very much as if they were threshing grain. Then Karlsevni exclaimed, " What can this mean? "

Snorri Thorbrandson answered, " It may be that this is a signal of peace, so let us take a white shield and lift it up before them."

So they did, while the others rowed up to them, gazed at them with astonishment, and then went on land. They were dark men and ugly, with unkempt hair on their heads. They had large eyes and broad cheeks. After they had stayed a while and marvelled, they rowed off to the south of the cape.

Karlsevni and his men had built their shelters above the lake, some of them close to the water, others farther away, and here they stayed that winter. There was no snow-fall whatever, and all their cattle grazed by themselves in the open.

But early one morning, as spring drew near, they saw

THE SKRAELINGS TASTE MILK

FOR THE FIRST TIME

THE BULL TERRIFIES THE SKRAELINGS

before their eyes a vast number of skin boats rowing
around the cape from the south. The bay was dotted with
them, as if it had been strewn with pieces of charcoal,
and on every one the sticks were waving. Karlsevni's men
raised their shields, and when the two parties met, they
started trading with each other.

These people wanted most of all to buy red cloth. They
also wanted to buy swords and spears, but that was forbidden by Karlsevni and Snorri. In exchange for the cloth
they offered untanned furs and grey pelts, and for each fur
they got a span's length [about nine inches] of the cloth,
which they tied around their heads. This went on for a
while, until the Norsemen began to run short of cloth.
Then they cut it into smaller strips, until each was no
more than a finger's width, and yet the Skraelings [as the
Norsemen called the savages] gave just as much for it or
even more.

In the Greenland Saga it is told that the Norsemen sold
the savages milk. Karlsevni asked the women to carry out
vessels of milk and other dairy products. At once the savages wanted to buy this and nothing else. So the trading
turned out in this way, that the savages carried their pur-
chases away in their stomachs, while Karlsevni and his men
had possession of their furs.

Then it happened that a bull belonging to Karlsevni
and his people ran out of the woods and bellowed furi-
ously. The savages were so terrified that they ran to their
boats, and rowed along the shore to the south. For three
weeks there was no trace of them. But at the end of this
time, a vast fleet of Skraeling boats hove into sight, rushing from the south like an angry torrent. This time the
savages were waving their sticks in a counter-sunwise
direction, and were yelling at the tops of their voices. This
time Karlsevni and his men took their red shields and held

them aloft. The savages leaped from their boats; the two
parties met and started fighting. It was a furious battle, for
the savages had warslings to help them. Karlsevni and
Snorri watched them lift up a pole with a huge knob on
the end, black in color, and about the size of a sheep's
belly, which flew up on land over the heads of the men,
and made a frightening noise when it fell. At this a great
fear seized Karlsevni and his followers, so that they thought
only of flight, and retreated up the stream. It seemed to
them that they were being attacked by savages on every
side, and this did not let up before they got back to some
cliffs, where they fought a hard battle.

Freydis came out and saw them retreating. She shouted
to them, " Why are you running away from these puny fel-
lows, fine men as you are! It looks to me as if you should
be able to cut them down like cattle. If I had weapons, I
think I could fight better than any of you! "

They paid no attention to what she was saying. She tried
to follow, but had trouble keeping up with them, for she
was with child. She went after them into the woods, and
the savages started towards her. In front of her lay a dead
man, Thorbrand, Snorri's son, whose head had been
crushed by a flat rock. Beside him lay his sword, and she
picked it up to defend herself. When the savages approached, she pulled out her breasts from under her dress
and slapped them with the naked sword. At this the savages were so appalled that they ran down to their boats
and rowed away.

Karlsevni and his men now came up to her and praised
her good fortune. Two men had fallen of his party, and a
great many of the savages, although the latter were far
superior in number. They now returned to their camp,
dressed their wounds, and talked over who the host might
be that had attacked them on land. It had seemed to them

FREYDIS DEFIES THE SKRAELINGS

as if there were two attacking parties, but now they saw that one of these must have been a delusion.

The savages found one of the dead with an axe beside him. One of them picked up the axe and hewed at a tree with it; one after the other tried it, and it seemed to them a great treasure because it cut so well. Then one of them took and struck a rock with it, so that the axe broke. They decided then that it was useless, since it could not withstand stone, and tossed it away.

Karlsevni and his men were now convinced that even though the country was richly endowed by nature, they would always live in dread and turmoil because of the enmity of those who lived there before. So they made ready to break up and return to their own country.

They sailed along the coast to the north. On the shore they found five savages asleep, dressed in leather jackets, and beside them vessels containing animal marrow mixed with blood. Karlsevni judged that these men must have been sent out as spies from this country, and killed them.

Later they found a cape that abounded in animals, and it looked as if the cape were solidly crusted with dung from all the animals that lay there at night. Then they reached Streamfjord, and there they found plenty of all they needed. Some say that Bjarni and Gudrid had stayed here with a hundred men and gone no farther, while Karlsevni and Snorri sailed to the south with forty men, stayed at Hop just two months, and returned the same summer.

Karlsevni set out with one ship to search for Thorhall the Hunter, while the others stayed in Streamfjord. They sailed north of Keelness, and then headed west, with the land on their port side. They found nothing but a forest wilderness, with hardly a clearing among the trees. When they had sailed a long time, they found a river running from east to west into the sea. Here they steered for the

river mouth and landed on the southern bank. [According
to the Karlsevni Saga, Thorvald Ericson was killed here
and not on that voyage of his own which has been recounted earlier.] After this they sailed away to the north
again.

They concluded that the mountains they found in this
country were the same as those they had seen at Hop, and
this belief was confirmed by the fact that the distance from
Streamfjord to both these places was the same. They returned to Streamfjord and lived there the third winter.

A D
1013

But this winter there was much quarreling among the
men; and women were the cause of it, for those who had
no women began attacking those who did. A son named
Snorri was born to Karlsevni the first autumn, and he was
three winters old when they left.

As they sailed away from Vinland, they got a favoring
south wind, and made their way to Markland. Here they
found five savages, — a bearded fellow, two women and
two children. Karlsevni and his men captured the boys,
but the rest got away and sank into the ground. They took
the boys along, taught them to speak, and baptized them.
The boys said that their mother was named Vethilldi and
their father Uvege. They said that kings ruled the land
of the Skraelings, and one of them was named Avalldama,
the other Avilldudida. They said there were no houses
there, and that people slept under rocks or in caves. They
said there was a country on the opposite side from their
own, where people went about in white clothes, uttered
loud cries, and carried poles with banners fastened to
them. It is generally believed that this must have been
White Men's Land or Greater Ireland. So they returned
to Greenland and stayed with Eric the Red that winter.

BATTLE WITH THE SKRAELINGS

Chapter XII

THE SAD FATE OF BJARNI GRIMOLFSON

Bjarni Grimolfson's ship was driven out to sea, to a place west of Ireland where the water was full of shipworms. Before they knew it, the ship was worm-eaten under them, and began to sink, so they had to hold counsel on what they should do. They had a jollyboat that was coated with sealtar and people say that the shipworm cannot attack wood that has been treated in this way. They started to enter the boat, but found that only half of the crew could get in.

Then Bjarni said, " There is room for no more than half of our men in the boat, and therefore I propose that we cast lots to decide who shall go. For this should not be decided according to rank." They all felt that this was so manful an offer that no one opposed it. When the lots were cast, Bjarni was in that half of the crew which was to go in the boat. But as the lucky ones were leaving the ship, a young Icelander who had been Bjarni's shipmate said to him, " Do you intend to desert me here, Bjarni? "

Bjarni answered, " It is so decided."

" This is not," said he, " what you promised my father, when we left Iceland together. Then you said that we two should share the same fate."

" I see no other way out," answered Bjarni, " or what would you propose? "

" I propose," said the other, " that we trade places, so that you come here and I go there."

" So be it," said Bjarni. " You come into the boat, and I shall go up on the ship, since you are so anxious to live and so fearful of death."

So they traded places, and Bjarni went on board the ship. Those who were in the boat sailed away until they reached Dublin in Ireland, and there they told this story. But it is generally believed that Bjarni and his companions perished in the wormy sea, for none of them was ever seen again.

FREYDIS UPBRAIDS HER HUSBAND, THORVARD

Chapter XIII

FROM THE GREENLAND SAGA

FREYDIS SEEKS HER FORTUNE

Once more people fell to talking of the journey to Vinland, for this seemed an open road to wealth and honor. The same summer that Karlsevni returned from Vinland, a ship arrived in Greenland from Norway. The skippers were two brothers, Helgi and Finnbogi, who were of Icelandic stock from the East Fjords. They spent the winter in Greenland.

A D
1013

Now it happened that Freydis, Eric's daughter, made a special trip from her home in Gardar to meet the brothers Helgi and Finnbogi. She proposed that they should sail to Vinland in their vessel, and share with her all the profits they might gain together. They agreed to this. Then she called on her brother Leif and asked if he would give her the houses he had built in Vinland. He answered that he would lend them to her, but would not give them away. Freydis and the brothers agreed that each of them should have thirty able-bodied men on board, besides women. But Freydis broke this agreement at once by taking along five extra men, whom she hid so the brothers knew nothing of it before they got to Vinland.

A D
1014

Now the two ships put out to sea, having agreed to stay together, if possible. There was no great distance between them, but the brothers arrived shortly before Freydis, and carried their baggage up to Leif's houses. When Freydis landed, her crew unloaded their ship and also began carrying their things up to the houses. Then Freydis exclaimed, " Why did you put your stuff in here? "

" Because we thought," said the brothers, " that you would live up to all our agreements."

" Leif lent these houses to me," said she, " not to you! "

Then Helgi remarked, " We brothers are no match for your wickedness! " They carried their belongings away and built a house of their own. They set it up farther from the sea, on the bank of the lake, and put it in fine order. Meanwhile Freydis was having timber cut down to fill her ship.

Now winter set in, and the brothers proposed that they should while away the time by playing games and entertaining each other. They did so for a while, but soon the men got to quarreling, the games were given up, and there were no more visits between the houses. This went on far into the winter.

Early one morning Freydis got out of bed and dressed, but did not put on her shoes. The weather was such that a heavy dew had fallen. She put on her husband's cloak, and then she went to the door of the house where the two brothers lived. Shortly before this a man had gone out and had left the door slightly ajar. She pushed it open, stood on the threshold a while, and said nothing. Finnbogi, who lay farthest from the door, was awake. He said, " What do you want here, Freydis? "

She answered, " I want you to get up and come out with me, so I can talk to you."

He did so, and they walked over to a log that lay near the house wall, and sat down on it.

" How do you like it here? " said she.

" It is a fine country," he answered, " with great re-

FREYDIS MURDERS THE WOMEN OF
THE EXPEDITION

sources, but I am troubled by the squabble that has grown up between us, for I can see no reason for it."

" There you spoke a true word," said she, " and I agree with you. But my errand is that I should like to trade ships with you brothers, for you have a larger ship than I, and I am anxious to get away from here."

" I shall agree to that," said he, " if it is your pleasure."

With these words they parted. She went home and Finnbogi back to his bed.

She got into bed with her cold feet, and awakened Thorvard with them, so that he asked why she was so cold and wet. She answered with great fury, " I went to see the brothers and asked them to sell me their ship, because I want a larger ship, but at that they lost their tempers, and they struck me and treated me roughly. But you are such a measly man that you would never avenge either my disgrace or your own. I am certainly finding out how far I am from Greenland. But if you do not avenge this, I am going to separate from you."

She kept it up until he no longer could bear her reproaches, and told his men to get up at once and seize their weapons. They did so, went to the brothers' house, and entered it while they were still asleep; they seized the men, tied them up, and led them out one by one. Freydis had each one killed as he came out, until all the men were dead; but no one would kill the women. Then cried Freydis, " Hand me an axe! " When she got it, she killed the five women herself, and left them dead.

After this monstrous deed, they returned to their house, and it was clear that Freydis thought she had managed very cleverly. She told her crew, " If we are lucky enough to reach Greenland again, I shall have any man killed who speaks of these doings. Our story will be that these people stayed on here after we left."

Early in the spring they rigged up the ship that the brothers had owned and filled it with all the products they could find, as much as the ship would carry. They had a good sailing and got back to Ericsfjord early in the summer. There lay Karlsevni's ship all ready to sail, just waiting for a fair wind. It is generally agreed that no ship has ever sailed from Greenland more richly laden than the one he commanded.

Freydis took up life again on her own farm, which had not been molested while she was gone. She gave her crew valuable gifts, for she wanted to hush up her crimes. But not all of the men were tightlipped enough to keep from talking about the misdeeds that had been committed. After a time the story leaked out and got to Leif, her brother, who was deeply distressed over it. He took three members of Freydis' crew and tortured them until they revealed all that had happened, and their stories tallied exactly.

" I do not have the heart," said Leif, " to punish my sister Freydis as she deserves, but I foresee that her descendants will enjoy little prosperity." It turned out as he said, for from that time on, no one thought anything but ill of them.

THROUGH TORTURE LEIF LEARNS

OF FREYDIS' GUILT

Chapter XIV

FROM THE KARLSEVNI SAGA AND
THE GREENLAND SAGA

KARLSEVNI AND GUDRID

RETURN TO ICELAND

In the meanwhile Karlsevni made his ship ready and sailed out to sea. He had a good voyage and got to Norway safely, and there he stayed all winter while he sold his cargo. Both he and his wife were shown the most courteous attention by the great men of Norway. The following spring he made ready to sail for Iceland, and when he was all prepared and his ship was waiting at the dock for a favorable wind, there came to him a German from Bremen in Saxony. He offered to buy Karlsevni's *husasnotra* [probably the ornamented ship's prow].

A D
1016

" It is not for sale," said he.

" I will give you half a mark in gold," said the German. Karlsevni thought this was a fine offer and sold it to him. The German went away with the *husasnotra,* but Karlsevni was unable to say what kind of wood there was in it. It was *mosur* from Vinland.

Now Karlsevni sailed away and touched land in the north of Iceland at Skagafjord, and there his ship was laid up for the winter. In the spring he bought a farm at Glaumbö and built himself a home. Here he lived the rest of his days and was greatly esteemed; many men of high regard have descended from him and his wife Gudrid. His mother thought he had made a poor match when he married Gudrid and would not live at home the first winter. But when she discovered what an exceptional woman Gudrid was, she returned, and the two women became the best of friends.

When Karlsevni died, Gudrid took over the management of the farm, together with her son Snorri, who had been born in Vinland. When Snorri was married, she went abroad and made a pilgrimage to Rome, and when she returned to her son Snorri's farm, he had built a church at Glaumbö. After that Gudrid took the veil, and lived there as a nun the rest of her life.

Snorri had a son named Thorgeir, the father of Yngvid, mother of Bishop Brand. A daughter of Snorri's was named Hallfrid, and she became the mother of Bishop Thorlak. Another son of Karlsevni and Gudrid was Bjorn, who became the father of Thorunn, the mother of Bishop Bjorn. Many men are descended from Karlsevni, for he was blessed with a great and honorable stock. He has told more fully than any one else the story of all these voyages, of which something has now been repeated. Here ends this saga.

GUDRID WITH SNORRI, THE FIRST

WHITE CHILD BORN IN AMERICA

SECTION II

THE EVIDENCE OF HISTORY —
A COMMENTARY ON
THE SAGA OF VINLAND

ADAM OF BREMEN

The first story of America came to Europe in a curiously roundabout way. It was embalmed in a great work of church history by a German schoolmaster who clearly never dreamt of its epochmaking possibilities. It had migrated to him by word of mouth from the very outposts of the known world, and by that time it sounded suspiciously like a fable of Cockayne. But he conscientiously put it down, for he had it from trustworthy men, and who was he to doubt their word, however strange it might sound?

His name was Adam, and he was head of the cathedral school at Bremen. He appears to have visited the court of Denmark not long after William of Normandy had crossed the Channel to make himself master of England. Adam eagerly gathered all the information he could about the history and geography of Scandinavia. His master, the archbishop of Hamburg, had designs on the newly converted souls of Scandinavia, and for the first time in world history the peoples of the North were exciting the friendly interest of medieval chroniclers. Adam wrote faithfully what he was told, and put it all in his *History of the Archbishopric of Hamburg*.

Adam reported a good many surprising facts about " the

islands of the North" and their inhabitants. He had
learned about the marvels of the midnight sun, the cold,
dark winters, and the strange peoples of Iceland, Greenland, and northern Norway. But strangest of all was the
story they told him of another "island," somewhere in
this northern sea, of a very different nature from the rest.
The King of Denmark himself told Adam that "there
was an island in that ocean visited by many, which is
called Winland, for the reason that vines grow wild there,
which yield the best of wine. Moreover, unsown grain
grows there in profusion, and this we know is not a fabulous fancy, for the accounts of the Danes prove that it is
a fact."

Written sometime around 1070, this is *the first authentic reference in world literature to the American continent.*

The king of Denmark who told Adam this story was
named Svein Estridson, and he was a nephew of Canute
the Great, erstwhile ruler of England, Denmark, and
Norway. But Svein was very unlike his uncle. He was not
a warrior, but a traveller and an observer, who found his
chief interest in a wise administration of his country.
Pope Gregory VII once addressed him as a man "well
versed in letters and zealous for the advancement of the
church." Adam was effusive in his praise of Svein: " He
retained in his memory all the deeds of the barbarians,
exactly as if they had been written." "All that we have
said or are going to say about the barbarians we have
learned from the accounts of this man." It is understand-
able why Adam included in his work even the statement
about the mysterious island somewhere in the Arctic with
vines and wild grain, though he clearly entertained doubts
about the truth of it.

But King Svein was right. He was one of those monarchs

of early Scandinavia who made a point of listening to the
tales of travelling poets and saga tellers. That such men
came to his court from Iceland and even far-away Greenland is attested by quite a different source. There is a
touching tale in the Icelandic sagas of one Audun, who
went to Greenland and spent all he owned on a polar bear
which he brought as a gift to King Svein in Denmark. For
all we know it may have been this very man who told Svein
the story of Vinland. But there were many others, too, of
these travelling Icelanders, who made their way at the
courts of continental Scandinavia by their very special
skill of narrative and fidelity of memory. They carried
from country to country a treasure of that prose and poetry which was the heritage of the Scandinavians. They
were the historians of their race, and they carried to the
European continent the first intimations that there was
unknown and unsuspected land to the west.

For we know now that two generations earlier men
from Iceland *had* been on the American coast. They
were not men who could write, but they were quick to
tell others what they had seen. They took their stories
back to Iceland, and from there the stories spread to Norway and Denmark. If we did not know this, it would be
hard to guess what Adam of Bremen meant by his brief
notice. As late as 1700, a learned Swedish scholar who did
not know the historical records of Iceland thought that
Adam's Winland was a mistake for Finland!

But when we learn that the intrepid sailor-explorers of
Iceland and Greenland applied the name " Vinland " to
a part of the American coast, and that the chief features
of this coast were its grapes and its wild wheat, then the
picture is suddenly illuminated, and we perceive the real
significance of Adam of Bremen's statement: his brief

account is the only contemporary testimony to the Norse discovery! But it is all we need, for Adam was a conscientious historian, not given to flights of fancy.

These few sentences in medieval Latin from the eleventh century clinch the central fact of our story: that the Norsemen were the first authenticated discoverers of America.

THE LEARNED MEN OF
ICELAND

When the chiefs of Iceland voted in the year 1000 to adopt Christianity as the law of their land, they were making history in more ways than they could have suspected. They were smashing the precedent established in most west European countries that the gospel of peace on earth could be spread only by blood and iron. More important was the fact that they were ushering in a new era in the history of their country. They were joining Iceland to the great cultural unity of Europe, so that it was no longer a land regarded as the last retreat of " barbarians " beyond the pale of human civilization. They were also voting into being a new class of men in Iceland — the hierarchy of the church. The first native Iceland bishop was ordained in 1056. Before long four monastery schools had been established. The church brought with it an art that was new to Iceland and that was going to be of tremendous significance to Icelandic culture: the art of writing on parchment.

It was not that the Scandinavians had never known how to write. They had a strange alphabet of their own, called the " runic," which they had learned from their Ger-

manic kinsmen to the south. But this was little used for
the writing of texts and messages. It was inscribed chiefly
on ornamental objects and monuments, with a magic and
religious significance. The stories and poetry of the vikings were not written; they were told from generation to
generation, learned and recited and learned again.

When the art of writing came to Iceland, it opened vast
new possibilities for the preservation of these traditions
without the inevitable loss that took place in oral trans-
mission. But there was one drawback; these traditions were
pagan, while the men who possessed the art were Christians. Everywhere else in northern Europe this conflict led
to the loss of the pagan traditions. The church thundered
against the black paganism of the people, and rooted it
out wherever possible. In Iceland it was different. By a
miracle of good luck, the sons of Icelandic chieftains who
took the oath of priesthood refused to extinguish the lights
of the past while taking over those of the new.

One of the first who used a Christian art to preserve
pagan lore was Ari, son of Thorgils, who was born in 1067,
about the time that Adam of Bremen was visiting the
friendly and learned king of Denmark. He was an orphan,
fostered by a proud old chief then approaching his eighti-
eth year. This venerable man was a lover of old tales and
traditions, and his memory reached back to the end of the
pagan age. The stimulus that he gave his foster son made
Ari a collector of traditions, and the first great historian
of his native land.

When he was about fifty years old, his superiors, the
two bishops of Iceland, asked him to write a survey of the
history of that country. Ari consented, and some time
between the years 1122 and 1133 he produced the first history of Iceland, and one of the first histories of any European country not written in Latin, but in the native tongue

of the land. Its chief distinction, however, is that it lacks entirely the medieval itch for the fabulous and the picturesque. Ari was a sober-minded, factual fellow, who named the sources of his information, and was much concerned about dates and other dry facts. In the annals of his country this book won him the honorable epithet of " Ari the Wise."

In one chapter of his work he digressed to tell the story of how Greenland was settled. After all, Greenland was still a diocese under Iceland, and her souls were vital to the Iceland bishops. Ari knew the name of the first Norse settler in Greenland, and he tells us where he got his information. An uncle of his had been in Greenland, and there he had talked to a man who had sailed out with Eric the Red way back in 986, a hundred and forty years before. But this man had told Ari's uncle more than that. He told him that when the first settlers got to Greenland, " they found human habitations, fragments of skin boats and stone implements from which it was evident that the same kind of people had lived there as inhabited Vinland and whom the Greenlanders called ' Skraelings.' "

Written around 1130, this is *the second authentic reference in world literature to America.*

Ari knew a great deal more about Vinland than he tells us here. He did not happen to be writing about that subject. He just alluded in passing to a place that everyone knew; there was no need of explaining where it lay or how it had been discovered. After all, the Icelandic annals of 1121 state that in that year one of the bishops of Greenland sailed out to look for Vinland.

Ari did not remain the only historian of Iceland. In the century that followed, historical writing blossomed luxuriantly in that little country. Pagan traditions crossed with clerical learning to produce one of the world's great

cultures. Around 1200 a grand compilation was made of
oral traditions current about Icelandic families and entitled " The Book of Settlement." In this attempt to give
the name of every important Icelandic settler and his gene-
alogy, Vinland is twice mentioned, quite as a matter of
course. In other written traditions of this period the story
of Vinland is repeatedly alluded to. And in 1347 the Icelandic annals tell about a ship that had drifted in to the
Iceland coast. It had started from Greenland, sailed to
Markland (the Norse name for another part of the American coast), and had then been driven off its course. This
is the last historical allusion to America in old Icelandic
literature.

Together, these allusions clearly show that from the
twelfth to the fourteenth century the learned men of Iceland knew that there were lands to the west of Europe
which had been visited by their countrymen. They had
names for these lands, and stories were current about their
inhabitants and their natural characteristics. But the allusions of the learned historians were mere footnotes to their
fascinating tale of Icelandic life. They would tell us little
about America if we did not also have the narratives of the
sagas to fill in the missing details. These narratives make
up the body of this volume, and to give them a proper
setting, we shall make an excursion into viking life and
viking traditions.

VIKING TRADITIONS

From the ninth century to the eleventh the North Atlantic
was a Scandinavian sea. Men from the Norwegian fjords
plied busily back and forth from Norway to the British
Isles, the Shetlands, the Faroes, the Hebrides, Iceland,
Greenland, and the American continent.

They were called " vikings " because they originally
made their homes in the sheltering bays (called " vik ")
of the North. Their small, swift-sailing vessels took the
pacified peoples of western Europe by surprise, for the vikings did not hesitate to use force. They greedily took
what they wanted — jewels, women, cattle, weapons,
money — all the beckoning glitter of a culture more re-
fined than their own. Their unconsecrated hands did not
even spare the bulging wealth of the Church, already
grown fat through the protective indulgence of royal
power. " Deliver us, O Lord," cried the terrified monks,
" from the fury of the Northmen! "

This grim, but picturesque view of the viking is deeply
enshrined in our American imagination, and is accurate
as far as it goes. But piracy and marauding were only one
aspect of viking life — the professional careers of a very
small number of chieftains. As coastal guards were
strengthened, and royal authority rose within the North,

viking piracy became an even rarer method of gaining
wealth. The transfer of goods from hand to hand took a
more peaceable course, as barter and commerce. New ave-
nues to wealth and fame were opened to those who could
take advantage of them. An illuminating story is told
about one Bjorn, son of Brynjolf, who lived in Sogn, a
famous Norwegian fjord. He wanted to get away from
home to forget an unhappy love affair, and asked his father
to fit him out with a warship and a crew so he could go
a-viking. But his father refused. Instead he gave him a
trading ship with a cargo of goods to Dublin, and said,
" *That* is now the most honorable voyage." Ancestral own-
ership of land was no longer the sole title to power, and
merchant careers like those of Einar of Thorgeir's Fell
and Thorfinn Karlsevni in our saga were made possible.

Unoccupied lands in the west also beckoned to those
who were uncomfortable amid the growing centralization
of authority. The viking movement became a great expansion of peoples, which brought Scandinavian populations
to Normandy in France, northern England, Scotland, Ireland, and the islands to the North. The Shetlands were the
first stepping stone, occupied in the eighth century; after
that came the Faroes and Orkneys, England and Ireland
(by 800), Iceland (about 870), Greenland (in 985 or
986), and America (around 1000).

While the viking vessels thus brought Scandinavians
to the rest of Europe, they also brought Europe to Scandinavia. They became the bond that tied Scandinavia to
western Europe. For these frail bottoms carried back to
the North new products of a southern culture, new ideas
and beliefs, new demands on life. For better or for worse,
the isolation of Scandinavia was at an end. In the year 1000
the chiefs of Iceland voted to adopt Christianity. Thirty
years later Olaf, the patron saint of Norway, was mar-

tyred in the struggle to convert his countrymen. The resistance of Germanic paganism was at length broken in its last strongholds, and the Church could enroll new converts in the majestic folds of its supernational organization. A period of restless and exciting activity came to an end. The viking expansion had reached a natural border; trade and travel had turned the vikings into Christian men, however thin the veneer that covered their turbulent temperaments.

But fortunately they did not completely forget their past. In Iceland, a remote corner of the Scandinavian area, they even clung to it with such tenacity that it survived the coming of a new faith and the passage of generations. Iceland was settled by emigrants from Norway, many of whom had first spent some time in the Norse settlements of the British Isles. These settlers were no poor, land-hungry emigrants; they were closely knit groups of friends and families, headed by proud chieftains who were unwilling to bow to changing circumstances in the homeland. In Iceland they set up the same aristocratic oligarchy that they knew from Norway, and a legal system in close imitation of the Norwegian. Only one feature did they expressly reject: the kingship, whose authority might menace their own. Instead they established one of the world's first parliaments — an annual meeting of all free citizens, directed by the chiefs and empowered to make laws and pass judgments, but not to execute them.

Iceland thus became a miniature Scandinavia, changing but little in the course of centuries. The fierce pride of the ruling families, the comparative isolation of Iceland from the strife of the Continent, and the stability of the social order led to an extraordinary interest in tradition. On long winter evenings the Icelandic household listened with fascination to tales of the great exploits of ancient

days, especially those exciting centuries before society settled down into the dull pattern of clerical ritualism. When
these events had originally occurred, none of the rough
and ready men who acted in them had been scholars. But
certain ones among them developed a special skill of memory and narration, which established them in the community as entertainers and as oracles of ancient wisdom.
As one generation of saga tellers died, new ones took up
the tradition and passed it on.

Such narration in far-away Iceland has been the means
of rescuing most of what we know today about the pagan
religion of our Germanic ancestors in England, Germany,
and Scandinavia, about Scandinavian history between 800
and 1200, and all that may truly be called Scandinavian
literature before 1300.

Most of this great body of verse and prose was written
down between 1100 and 1300 by men with clerical train-
ing. It had then been current in oral narration anywhere
from one to three hundred years. Its contents range from
fantastic adventure to the soberest reality, all comprised
under the term " saga " — which means only " that which
is said " and was applied to all prose narrative.

But the Icelanders had a sharp sense of the difference
between sagas: they knew whether they were dealing with
truth or fiction. They had some sagas they called " lying
sagas " or " stepmother sagas," and one Norwegian king
admitted that he found these the most entertaining. But
those sagas that really touched their own or their ancestors' lives were of a different nature. They were told in the
full conviction that they had really happened, and were
the more real the closer their scene of action lay to Iceland,
the center of the Icelander's universe. The most vivid and
credible were the Icelandic Family Sagas, which pictured
the clan feuds of Iceland between 870 and 1000. Next

to these came the sagas of the Norwegian kings between 870 and 1200, with inserted adventures of Icelanders throughout the Norwegian colonies of the North Atlantic. As soon as the narrative moved out of this period or this area, its events grew fabulous and improbable.

Students have asked again and again: how could the Icelanders possibly have preserved through three centuries any accurate information about the deeds of their ancestors without the help of writing? There have been voices like those of the skeptical Lord Raglan, who airily declared of the sagas that " their principal incidents are mythological." Some devout admirers of the saga have gone to the opposite extreme of holding each word to be that of inspiration. They have taken it for granted that the stories as we have them were composed shortly after the events, and that by some prodigious feat of memory the Icelanders learned them by heart generation after generation until a man of letters came to fasten them to parchment.

Amid the clamor of believers and skeptics the scholars have spent many conscientious hours trying to unravel fact from fiction in the sagas. They have combed archives for contemporary sources and they have excavated material objects of the viking age. They have checked the sagas with each other, working out their chronology, and seeing how it dovetails with dates from other sources. A comparison has been made with similar traditions in modern Norway, where documents are available to check the narrative.

Out of this labor has come confirmation that historical facts *can* be preserved in folk tradition over a surprisingly long period. But people must have some reason for so preserving them, and special conditions of social life must be present to keep the tradition from swerving too far from fact. Such conditions did exist among the Icelanders, by virtue of their family pride, their isolation from the rest of the world, and the smallness of their communities. Family pride was no academic matter; one's family tree was a patent of nobility, a source of strength in the community. Isolation prevented the mass of new, fresh material from overwhelming the old to the same extent as it does in modern life. The narrowness of the group led to close contact between people; the truth could not be concealed, for every one knew about every one else; private secrets were not easy to keep.

The sagas as we know them are certainly a species of literature, and they owe their artistic qualities largely to the age that wrote them down. The pattern as a whole is that of Christian Iceland of the twelfth and thirteenth centuries. But the bits out of which these mosaics were woven are traditional facts from the pagan communities of an earlier day. The roots of the sagas go back to the sort of tales that pass in every community about the doings of its citizens. A dash of gossipy narrative, a bit of journalistic exaggeration, the earthy humor of a local commentator, perhaps some family backbiting — these were the elements out of which a chain of skillful story-tellers welded their sagas. Where information failed, imagination might come to the rescue and supply repartee, secret decisions, hidden motives, childhood escapades, and dramatic dénouements. The value of such talk for historical purposes depends entirely on the information and the accuracy of the original story-tellers. The historical sagas are therefore not strictly factual and analytic history in the modern sense. They are tales of historic events, undeniably colored by the interests of generations of story-tellers and listeners, and the more accurate the closer they are to the original events in time and place.

The story of Vinland was not one of the central tales of Icelandic tradition. It was not among the earliest to be written down, and its events took place in a distant land, far out on the rim of the Norse world. It was not easy for its facts to remain unconfused. But it did involve the ancestors of a distinguished Icelandic family, who had an interest in keeping it alive. More than this, it contained the history of how Iceland's only colony, Greenland, was settled, a tale of great interest as long as relations were continually maintained.

It is by the interplay of all these factors of human effort and human error that the sagas have become what they are today: intensely vivid tales, full of the life of bygone days, true in substance, but subject to human vagary. Of such stuff is woven the story of ancient Vinland.

THE TWO VERSIONS

Paper was practically unknown in Iceland before 1600, but there were plenty of sheep, whose skins could be turned into parchment. In spite of smoke and damp, vandalism and the tooth of time, the Icelanders have managed to rescue some seven hundred vellum manuscripts from their medieval past. Most of these have now found their way to Copenhagen. They date all the way from 1150 to 1550, but relatively few of them are originals written in the early part of this period. After 1300 the copying of older manuscripts became a regular industry.

In those days of expensive bookmaking, books were treasures, and some of the wealthy men of Iceland were anxious to build up impressive libraries. They hired scribes to copy whatever manuscripts they could lay their hands on and to compile elegant new volumes. It often mattered less what the books contained than that they were beautifully written and attractively illuminated. The results were among the finest specimens of Icelandic bookmaking, treasured in Icelandic families for generations. The farmer who owned the Flatey Book in the seventeenth century would not part with it for five hundreds of land.

Three of these compilations happen to include the sur-

viving accounts of Norse voyages to Vinland. The oldest
was written around 1330 for a noted Icelandic and Norwegian dignitary named Hauk Erlendson, a descendant
of Thorfinn Karlsevni; after him it bears the name
" Hauk's Book." The next was written between 1387 and
1394 for Jon Hakonarson, an Icelandic squire, and is the
largest and best preserved of all Icelandic manuscripts.
In the seventeenth century, when it was rediscovered, it
was owned by a family living at Flatey (Flat Island) in
Broadfjord; for this reason it is known as the " Flatey
Book." The third and youngest dates from the first half of
the fifteenth century, and bears no other name than its
catalogue number in the Arnamagnean Library in Copenhagen, AM. 557, 4to.

All of these are copied from earlier manuscripts, probably going back to the thirteenth century. The first
contains a saga which is entitled " Thorfinn Karlsevni's
Saga " (though only in a late hand). The second contains
two sections inserted into a saga of King Olaf Trygvason,
one of which is entitled " Tale of the Greenlanders." The
third contains a saga entitled " Saga of Eric the Red." Of
these the first and third are practically the same; the dif-
ferences are only such as might have been caused by
scribes and copyists. We shall unite these under the title
of the " Karlsevni Saga," because they deal chiefly with
the exploits of Thorfinn Karlsevni. The second saga,
which appears in the Flatey Book, we shall call the
" Greenland Saga." These two versions stand in the sharp-
est contrast.

The Greenland Saga tells us that the first man to sight
American shores was one Bjarni Herjulfson, while the
Karlsevni Saga says that it was Leif Ericson. According to
the Greenland Saga, Leif's discovery was a planned expedition, but according to Karlsevni's Saga it was an acci-

dent. The former gives a detailed account of Leif's voyage, while the latter concentrates on Karlsevni. The former also tells about separate voyages made by Leif's brother, Thorvald, and his half-sister Freydis. The latter insists that the others accompanied Karlsevni on *his* voyage.

These and other discrepancies show that two separate traditions were current in Iceland about the Vinland voyages. The one found in the Karlsevni Saga was the generally accepted one in Iceland, as we see from certain references in other sagas. The sagas of the Norwegian kings, including Snorri Sturluson's *Heimskringla,* take it as a fact that Leif Ericson was blown out of his course on the way home from Norway in the year 1000 and found Vinland on this trip. This appears to be the official version, probably kept alive by the distinguished descendants of Thorfinn Karlsevni and Gudrid. Quite isolated from this tradition and without any apparent influence in either direction stands the account of the Greenland Saga. This story is less interested in Karlsevni and concentrates on the family of Eric the Red in Greenland. It has been suggested that perhaps this saga lived at first in Greenland and was later brought to Iceland.

During the past half century a bitter debate has been waged concerning the relative merits of these two versions. Until 1887 there was a general preference for the Greenland Saga, but in that year the Norwegian historian Gustav Storm vigorously attacked this version and insisted on the superior accuracy and consistency of the Karlsevni Saga. Specialists in Icelandic literature have in general supported this view (Jónsson, Thórðarson, Hermannsson) . Other students of the subject, however, whose approach has been less purely literary (Hovgaard, Gathorne-Hardy, Brøgger) have been unwilling to dismiss the Greenland Saga in so cavalier a fashion. Their attitude has been that of Professor "Hovgaard: " The truth probably lies between the two sagas."

This much is certain: in their eagerness to assert the superiority of the Karlsevni Saga, its advocates have over-shot their mark. It is true that the Karlsevni Saga stands close to the historical family sagas of Iceland, while the Greenland Saga in certain respects is reminiscent of the so-called " Lying " or " Fabulous " Sagas. But to maintain, as some do, that the Greenland Saga is only a con-fused reminiscence of the other, or to heap lofty sarcasm on its weaknesses is a fall into the opposite extremity. One eminent authority can even bring himself to write that Tyrker is " of course, a caricature of Thorhall Hunts-man," though the similarities are insignificant. Some of the weaknesses these writers bring up against the Green-land Saga are imaginary, as their assertion that Tyrker was drunk when he brought the grapes back, or that Leif loaded his ship with grapes in the spring. Both of these are inferences which the text does not support. These writers also have a tendency to minimize the weaknesses of the Karlsevni Saga, its story of unipeds (not included in the present version), its illusory Indian attackers, its strange Scotch runners with the names Haki and Hekja, its moun-tains in Vinland, Leif's gallant adventure in the Heb-rides, the two Skraeling boys and their mythical Greater Ireland.

Even the most confirmed opponents of the Greenland Saga admit that there are certain " reminiscences of genu-ine tradition " in it. There are statements and episodes in it which can only go back to stories by those who acted in them. If so, it is extremely unlikely that those who told this saga needed to draw on the Karlsevni Saga at all, or had ever heard of it. They were out of touch with Ice-landic saga tradition, and lacked the means of checking up on certain facts of chronology. But they were better informed on what happened in the family of Eric the Red than was the official Icelandic tradition.

When the two versions agree, it is therefore a double confirmation of historical accuracy. When they disagree, it is partly due to a difference in stress and point of view. The Karlsevni Saga is the story of an Icelandic family, polished off with all the refinement of its literary type. The Greenland Saga is a tale of exploration and adventure, more episodic, and inclined to stress the miracles and surprises of the amazing new country beyond the seas.

THE LAND OF ERIC THE RED

A papal letter written in 1492 declares that "Greenland lies at the end of the world." Few Americans realize that since its first exploration by Eric the Red in 982, Greenland was well-known as the extreme outpost of European civilization. It appears regularly on medieval maps, and throughout the Middle Ages commercial and ecclesiastical contact with the European continent was maintained. For nearly five hundred years a very considerable Norse colony supported life on a strip of western coast between a stormy sea and the vast inland ice of Greenland.

American discovery begins with the story of this colony, for Greenland was the last stepping stone in the Norse trek across the North Atlantic. The explorers and colonizers who reached out to the American continent were sons and friends of the man who settled Greenland.

But Greenland is itself a part of the New World, and the story of its discovery and settlement a part of American history. It also deserves a place in our narrative for its own intrinsic fascination. On the western coast of Greenland are still visible the ruins of the first structures built by white men in the western hemisphere. These have been excavated by the hundreds, and shown to be the sites of Norse churches, farm houses, and barns. Their skeletons,

implements, jewels, inscriptions, and even clothing are
vivid confirmations of the story told in Iceland's ancient sagas. Modern Danish archeologists have made the
frozen soil of Greenland yield up a record of viking life
more vivid and complete than that found in any other
part of the Scandinavian world.

It all began with one of those lucky accidents that
marked exploration in an age when sailors were wholly
at the mercy of the wind and the stars. Sometime after
900 a certain Gunnbjorn was on his way to Iceland, but
blew out of his course and sighted land to the west of
Iceland. A generation earlier Iceland itself had been discovered in exactly the same way. Gunnbjorn must have
seen something of the rocky, ice-bound eastern coast of
Greenland, and found it too uninviting for further exploration. His discovery was known, however, and talked
about in Iceland; but there was too much available land
in Iceland for any one to bother.

Many years passed, and Gunnbjorn's Reefs were still
unexplored. Icelandic society began settling into a relatively stable pattern, and the age of pioneering was over.
About 960 a chief in southwestern Norway named Thorvald got into trouble with his neighbors, and found it advisable to emigrate to Iceland. He and his son Eric found
nothing to settle on but a bleak shore in the extreme
northwest of Iceland. Eric, nicknamed " the Red," probably from the color of his hair, had no taste for this kind
of inferiority. He married a girl from a more southerly
district, cleared a farm in the prosperous valley of Hawkdale, and started to work his way up. But he had terrific
odds against him, surrounded by well-established and hostile chiefs, who relished no upstarts. They succeeded in
getting him banished from Hawkdale, and he had to flee
to some unprofitable islands in the mouth of the fjord,

where he took up an uncertain and temporary residence.

These events are all related in the first chapter of our saga, which is devoted to the figure of Eric and the great decision which grew out of his troubles in Iceland. Eric was outlawed a second time, now from all Iceland; not because his crimes were so outrageous, but because his friends were less powerful than his enemies. In a system of family alliances and enmities, with constant maneuvering for power, Eric got the worst of it. But this defeat brought out the real character of the man: he did not turn to viking piracy, and he did not try to court the favor of kings and chiefs in the older settlements. Instead he decided to spend the three years of his banishment exploring new lands and opening up new possibilities.

After a touching goodbye to his friends and supporters, he set off on one of the most amazing voyages of exploration on record. He hove into sight of the impassable east coast of Greenland and followed it southwards, until he rounded the southern tip and at length found inhabitable land. Here he systematically explored the coast and its fjords through three summers and winters. The shore he found was not radically different from that of western Norway and Iceland; he saw that in spite of its vast distance from home, and its bleak, treeless aspect, it was well adapted to human life. His enthusiasm was so infectious that he was able to spread it to others when he got back to Iceland. His propaganda tactics (which included even the detail of an attractive name: Greenland) were so successful that several hundred settlers accompanied him on his voyage of settlement. That nearly half of them were shipwrecked is only additional evidence of what difficulties and dangers Eric had had to overcome in successfully opening up this new land to Norse settlement.

In Greenland Eric's qualities found their fulfillment.

He became the honored patriarch of a settlement that
eventually grew to include some three thousand inhabitants. They were grouped in two sections, the Eastern Settlement where Eric lived, and farther to the north the
smaller Western Settlement. Eric lived to see his sons
grow up into hardy explorers, who followed his example
by pushing on to new lands still farther afield. One of
them was even received at the Norwegian court, and given
a royal commission to make Christians out of the heathen
Greenlanders. But this intrusion upon his patriarchal authority Eric resented. He grumpily told his son Leif that
the good deed he had committed by rescuing a shipwrecked crew was offset when he brought " this faker " —
the priest — to Greenland. For all he could do, the new
doctrines intruded themselves squarely into his own
home. His wife built the first church in Greenland right
on their farm, and applied direct personal pressure on
Eric to abandon his paganism. The saga describes the
agony of Eric's dilemma, in terms that are restrained but
very pointed.

From this beginning the Church grew to be a real power
in Greenland. Sixteen parish churches were built, all of
stone; in 1112 the first bishop of Greenland left Iceland
to visit his new see. At Gardar in the Eastern Settlement
a cathedral was built, ninety feet long and fifty feet wide,
with glass windows and a timbered gable. In one of its
chapels there was found in 1926 the skeleton of a bishop,
with a plain gold episcopal ring on his ring finger, and
in his right hand a bishop's crozier, a stick of ash with an
iron ferrule at one end and a beautifully carved head of
walrus ivory at the other. Bishops were reluctant to make
the long and arduous voyage to Greenland, certainly an
unprofitable see. Yet throughout the centuries of its existence the Greenland colony maintained its Christian

customs of worship and burial. " The dead lie piously with folded arms, and not infrequently with a small wooden cross in the hands or on the breast." Runic inscriptions on these crosses often tell the names of the dead, and commend them to God. But they also reveal that the practice of pagan magic described in our saga did not die out with the coming of Christianity.

Today Eskimos roam the fields that once were populated by Norsemen. But there were no Eskimos in this part of Greenland when the Norsemen came, nor for several centuries afterwards. However simple and primitive the life of the Norse settlers must have been, it was not like that of the Eskimos. The Eskimos were nomads, who lived on fish and game; they roamed over a wide area to find their food. The Norsemen could use these products only to supplement their diet; they were a settled, agricultural people, basically dependent on dairy produce. When Eric explored Greenland, he had to be on the lookout for those green spots in the inner fjords that meant pasturage and fodder for cattle. In these inlets between the sea and the glacier the Norsemen raised cows, sheep, goats, and pigs in great numbers. The excavations of Eric's farm alone show four barns, with room for forty cows. No wonder that in the thirteenth century a Norwegian scribe could write, " It is said that in Greenland there are good pastures and there are large and good farms, for there they have many cattle and sheep, and there they make much butter and much cheese; they live on these mainly, and also on meat and game of many kinds, reindeer meat, whale meat, seal meat, and bear meat."

At its best, life in Greenland was very much like that of the other Norse colonies of the North Atlantic. Our saga describes the jolly winter spent at Brattahlid by

Thorfinn Karlsevni and his men. Excavations have
brought to light neatly carved chessmen of whale bone
and walrus ivory with which they must have whiled away
many idle hours. Clothing found in the graves bears testimony that men and women tried to follow the styles of
their contemporaries in Europe. One of the poems of the
Elder Edda claims to have been composed in Greenland,
and it may be true, for the poem incongruously intro-
duces a polar bear into the epic tale of the Nibelungs.
Even on this remote shore the poetic vein of the viking
bards could find expression, as is confirmed by the verse
of our saga.

The difference between this and the other Norse colonies was that life in Greenland was more precariously
poised. Grain could not grow there; iron was extremely
scarce; wood for fuel and building had to be imported or
found as driftwood. The Icelandic annals report that in
1189 there came to Iceland a Greenland ship which was
held together almost wholly by wooden nails and whale
bone. For a long time the chief product of Greenland that
could be bartered for the products of European civilization was walrus ivory. This was supplemented with seal
hides and live polar bears. But toward the end of the Middle Ages the Greenland products lost out in the compe-
tition of other wares; walrus ivory gave way to elephant
tusks from Africa. The colony was no longer so tempting
to commercial enterprise.

In the meanwhile political conditions in the homeland
were rapidly changing. In 1397 Norway entered into a
union with Sweden and Denmark which drew her attention away from the North Atlantic colonies. Since 1261
the Greenlanders had been subject to the Norwegian
king, and he had promised to send them two ships a year;
it was forbidden for others to trade with them. But in

1349 Scandinavia was ravaged by the Black Death; a general impotence fell over these countries, and from 1367 there is no record that any royal ship ever left for Greenland. In 1408 a party of Icelanders was blown off its course and landed in Greenland. They are the last Icelanders known to have visited the Greenland colony. At this time the Western Settlement was already blotted out, and a new menace threatened the Norsemen, the Eskimos. From the middle of the thirteenth century they had been pressing southward. Although their methods and equipment for fighting were inferior to those of the Norsemen, they had the advantage of greater numbers.

But by the fifteenth century the Norsemen themselves were not the hardy specimens of manly perfection that had harried Europe five centuries before. The skeletons from Greenland graveyards that have been excavated and minutely analyzed by Danish scientists tell an amazing tale of malnutrition and degeneration. All indications point to a lowering of vitality due to a worsening of climate. A few bad years would be enough to wipe out the margin that made life possible. Their height was down to five feet; their life span to thirty; their skeletons were malformed, atrophied, constricted, until their women could no longer bear children; their teeth were worn down and their brain capacities reduced. In the words of Professor Nørlund, "They had become an inactive flock of debilitated individuals, undersized and deformed."

Yet the Eastern Settlement must have lingered on toward the end of the fifteenth century, when the attention of Europe was again directed to the west. Some of them may have been alive when Columbus set out for the Indies. In 1519 Christiern II, King of Denmark and Norway, made plans for " sending a huge fleet to win back Greenland from the heathen." But contact with Greenland was not again established until the Englishman John Davis went ashore years later, in 1585. In 1721 a Norwegian missionary, Hans Egede, went to Greenland in the hope of finding his old countrymen and winning them back to the true faith; but he stayed to become the apostle of the Eskimos.

The chain that had tied the Norse settlements of the North Atlantic together had been too weak. Greenland was broken off, and it is no wonder that the very last link, America, was entirely lost in the gathering dust of time.

VOYAGES TO VINLAND

The Norsemen found America in just the same way that they had found Iceland and Greenland, and before that the Shetlands and the Faroes: by a combination of luck and skill. Wind and storm drove the viking boats out of their familiar channels into sight of new shores. Reports of the survivors were eagerly heard by enterprising men who saw a chance of wealth and adventure in the search for new lands. After the discoverers and explorers came the settlers, who set out with friends and family, goods and livestock to make their homes in greener pastures. This had been the pattern of each preceding step in viking expansion, but only for Vinland do we have a detailed picture of the whole process, lighted by human episodes. That Naddod who first sighted Iceland and that Gunnbjorn who first saw Greenland are only names; but Bjarni Herjulfson is vividly real to us, because he lived within the age rescued to our gaze by the Icelandic Saga.

Bjarni was a merchant viking, who carried goods in his own ship between Norway and Iceland — sealskins, wool, down, and fish from Iceland in exchange for wine, grain, iron, and timber from Norway. He was a skillful mariner, willing to try a course he had never sailed for the sake of being with his father. But the weather blew him far to

the south of Greenland, his destination. He may have
drifted as far as the New England coast, which he knew
was not Greenland because it bore the wrong aspect and
faced the wrong way. The coast sloped to the north and
east, so he set sail in the only direction he could take to
reach a likelier shore. He did not need to hug the coast,
for a skilled seaman can sense its presence even when it is
out of sight. He probably skirted Nova Scotia and Newfoundland, and then struck boldly across Davis Strait to
his destination.

Nothing was done about his discovery in Greenland
until Leif, a son of the patriarchal Eric, grew old enough
to start sailing. He showed a boldness worthy of his stock
by sailing straight across to Norway without the usual stop
in Iceland. It was the first non-stop sail of the Atlantic,
slightly marred by a forced landing in the Hebrides, and
a subsequent gallant adventure. His purpose in Norway
was that of so many Icelandic chiefs' sons: to be presented
at court and gain the wealth and prestige resulting from
the king's favor. But this king was different from the
earlier ones. This Olaf had taken up a new religion and
made this faith a condition of his favor. Olaf Trygvason
did not hesitate to imprison and put to death those who
defied his missionary zeal. Shortly before this he had
rounded up all the leading Icelanders in Trondheim and
held them as hostages for the conversion of Iceland. Leif
had his qualms about trying to spread the new gospel of
peace on earth in Greenland, for he knew his father. But
the king managed to persuade him, and so Leif took over
the rôle of missionary.

Now it is uncertain whether Leif found America acci-
dentally on his way home, as the Karlsevni Saga says, or
whether he made a special voyage of exploration later,
as the Greenland Saga says. Here the two versions part

company. In the former case the discovery was made in
1000 A.D., as most other Icelandic sources insist; in the
latter case it was not before 1002.

Leif was a man of the kind that the Norsemen admired;
the epithet "lucky," which he got by rescuing a shipwrecked crew, was a word of greater depth and significance in those days. The king alluded to Leif's luck, and
Leif later declared that his father Eric had this quality;
their luck was not an accident, but was felt to be the result of very real gifts and abilities. It is in connection with
Leif's voyage that we first hear the familiar Norse names
applied to the various parts of the American coast: Helluland, which may have been Newfoundland or Labrador;
Markland, which may have been Nova Scotia; and Vinland, which was probably somewhere in New England.
We shall see later why these identifications are so vague
and uncertain.

These new discoveries made a great stir in Greenland.
The settlements buzzed with excited talk about exploration. A dream of happier circumstances rose before viking
eyes — the dream of a country flowing with wine and
wheat, amazing for its gentle winters, full of wood for
their houses and feed for their cattle. But it soon appeared
that the dream was not going to be too easy to realize.
Thorvald, a brother of Leif's, was the first to pay for it
with his life. He led an expedition in 1004, if we can rely on
the Greenland Saga, but in the second year of his absence
he met the natives, and fell a victim to their arrows. His
men returned in 1007, and the following year a third
brother, Thorstein, made the same attempt. But he, too,
seems to have lacked his brother Leif's and his father
Eric's luck, for he was driven about by storms all summer
and never caught sight of Vinland.

Then a new figure comes into prominence in our

saga, an Icelandic merchant named Thorfinn the Promising (Karlsevni). According to the reckoning of the
Greenland Saga he got to Greenland in 1009; the Karlsevni Saga is less definite, requiring only that he get there
after 1002. Karlsevni belonged to a wealthier and more
powerful society than did the Greenlanders; in a pinch
he could even do a good turn to their chief, Eric the Red.
He had what the Greenlanders lacked, the capital with
which to equip a true expedition of settlement. His purpose in coming to Greenland was simply to make a good
deal; but the exciting news he got there turned his mind
to a new and greater enterprise.

There is something impressive about this expedition,
with its three ships and its hundred and sixty men. It was
more than a raid, or a jaunt of adventure; there were
women and cattle aboard, regular equipment for a permanent settlement. The Greenland Saga specifically says
that " they planned to settle in this county, if it were possible." There were both Icelanders and Greenlanders
along, and among the crew and its leaders such miscellaneous personalities as the noble Bjarni Grimolfson and
the glowering, but indispensable pagan Thorhall.

Karlsevni followed a different route from that of his
predecessors; he chose to start from Greenland's Western Settlement, and must therefore have hit the American
coast farther to the west and north, probably somewhere
in Labrador. He coasted along its shore to the southeast,
and his Markland may well have been somewhere in
Labrador or Newfoundland. From here on the saga gives
such intricate and confusing sailing directions that it is
quite likely he sailed through the Strait of Belle Isle into
the Gulf of St. Lawrence. Here he spent his first, unfortu-
nate winter in America. The men were so busy exploring
that they gathered no supplies for the winter, probably ex-

pecting that the winter would be mild. But it turned out to
be very severe, and the saga pictures their unhappy predic-
ament. There were no grapes, and this was clearly not the
Vinland they had heard about. Thorhall's sarcastic verses
express the dissatisfaction of many in the party. But in
the spring Karlsevni made his way out of this area, probably around Nova Scotia and down the coast of New England and Leif's Vinland.

Here he met his first savages. Discouraged by the dis-
astrous encounter, he retreated to the original camp in
the more secure Streamfjord. He sought the lost Thorhall
in the inner parts of the Gulf, but in vain. On his way
home he picked up a couple of savages, mere lads, who
may have been either Eskimos or Indians. In any case it
is a mistake to make anything out of their supposed babblings. Then he sailed across Davis Strait again to his destination in the Eastern Settlement of Greenland, reaching it in 1013 as the Greenland Saga reckons.

While the voyage itself bears all the marks of authentic
history, there is an air of imaginative embroidery about
some of its details. The story of how Freydis terrified the
Indians is an amusing piece of Icelandic slapstick, selected
by one of the saga narrators for its effective character por-
trayal. But it has been shown by Stefán Einarsson that this
episode may reflect more ancient beliefs, the magic fear
inspired in primitive peoples by the violation of a taboo.
Similar behavior is recorded in Irish literature, among the
ancients by Plutarch, and is reported in our own day from
the Lapps of northern Europe. Cú Chulainn, the Irish
hero, was one of those whose strength was sapped at the
sight of feminine nakedness.

There still remains a voyage of quite a different character from the others, so base and senselessly cruel that many
regard it as a mere invention. In the Flatey Book version

Freydis is said to have sailed to Vinland in 1014 and returned in 1015 after the foulest and most unmotivated
murder spree in all Icelandic literature. Her earlier exploits against the Indians were amazing, even amusing;
this tale is sheer horror. It violates both decency and prob-
ability, and Leif's acquiescence is utterly un-Icelandic.
In her amazonic strength of character, however, she does
not stand alone among Norse women of ancient days.
Their position was a privileged one, and their influence
on history could more than once be baneful enough. Such
was Hallgerd in the Saga of Burnt Njal, who refused to
give her husband a lock of her hair to mend his bowstring,
even though his life depended on it, — because she remembered an insult he had offered her years before.

Whatever we think of Freydis and her harshness, we
must see in the portrait of her character one of the many
striking depictions offered us by the saga. We cannot now
say how much is history and how much is art in these descriptions, but all of them help to build up an unforget-
table picture of ancient Norse life. We see Eric, undaunted
by men but subdued by his wife's passive resistance, the
patriarch of his colony but troubled to think that a chance
visitor would go back to Iceland and complain of the enter-
tainment. We are amused by the German Tyrker, who is
so excited by his discovery of the grapes of his childhood
that he relapses into his native tongue, and by Thorhall
who calls on the Thor for whom he has been named to
produce a whale, only to find that it poisons the cooks.
We are impressed by the noble Gudrid, whose son Snorri
was the first white child known to have been born in
America, and who managed the rare feat of winning over
her mother-in-law. That she took the veil and went to
Rome is certainly an anachronism, and was probably invented by one of the three bishops who descended from

her. The decision of Bjarni Grimolfson to perish rather than break a promise he had made is entirely in keeping with the stern ethics of ancient Norse life.

The sagas grew up in an age of struggle between primitive beliefs and the organized church of Christendom. The description of the witch whom Gudrid assisted is classic for the insight it gives into pagan Norse folklore. Its elaborate detail and sumptuousness of display forbid us from believing that it really took place in primitive Greenland. But even if we grant that some later admirer of Gudrid inserted it here to glorify his heroine, this dramatic picture of Norse witchcraft is none the less substantially true. In the story of Thorstein Ericson's death we make the acquaintance of Iceland's exceedingly substantial ghosts. When Eric the Red refused to start on a voyage because it opened with a bad omen, he was obeying ancient beliefs. Eric represents in his person the spirit of the old gods, whose worship was closely tied to the family structure and was a prerogative of the viking chiefs. But he was doomed to defeat, for Greenland could not refuse to follow the times; its economic and social welfare was tied up with religious conformity.

Again and again we are reminded that the voyages to Vinland were not undertaken for the sheer love of adventure and exploration. There is constant allusion to something called in Old Norse " landskostir," the natural advantages of the land, which we have variously translated as " natural character," " the generosity of nature," and " resources." These were very real advantages, which contributed directly to the support of human life and to the increase of human wealth. As the Greenland Saga quite frankly puts it, " People were talking of the journey to Vinland, for this seemed an open road to wealth and honor." Places that could be lived in, and products that

could be turned to advantage, this was what Vinland
seemed to offer above all others. Even the chilly Streamfjord satisfied the basic requirements of Scandinavian existence in the colonies of the North Atlantic, for did it not
furnish " game on the mainland, birds' nests on the island,
and fish in the sea "?

The relations between Norsemen and the American
natives are among the most colorful and convincing features of the saga narratives. Both versions agree that these
relations began with friendly barter and ended in de-
structive battle. It has been justly said that these encoun-
ters were the first between Europeans and savages in the
modern world. They form a very instructive introduction
to European colonial history. Without any previous train-
ing in how to treat natives, the Norsemen showed all the
traits of greed, unfairness, and exploitation that have characterized European colonial expansion. Both versions
show, though in different ways, how the Norsemen failed
to give the savages full value for their goods. They show
the naïve wonder of the savages at such unheard-of phenomena as iron weapons, red cloth, milk, and fiery bulls.
They also show the mobility and warlike quality of these
savages, and the cruel measures to which the Europeans
resorted to protect themselves from their fury.

Most of the details of Skraeling life given in the sagas
can be verified among the Indians of eastern America.
John Cabot wrote of the Indians he met that " they use in
war bows, arrows, darts, lances, wooden clubs, and slings."
The mysterious ball which the Skraelings threw at the
Norsemen is explained by H. R. Schoolcraft, an authority
on the Ojibwa Indians, who says that they used a large
instrument of war consisting of a large heavy stone
wrapped in an animal pelt and put on a pole; Schoolcraft
calls it a " balista," which tallies with the saga. As School-

craft puts it, " brought down among a group of men on a sudden it produced consternation and death." Henry Hudson tells about the Indians that " they brought many beaver skinnes and other fine furres, which they would have changed for redde gownes." This might have been taken right out of the Karlsevni Saga. The food of the sleeping savages, animal marrow mixed with blood, suggests the " moose-butter " made of moose bones by the Indians and used as provision on their journeys, according to one early writer on Nova Scotia. The skin-covered boats sound like Eskimo kayaks, but were entirely different in construction and purpose. The Norsemen might have mistaken birchbark for skin on a hasty inspection; but there are also said to be Indian tribes who cover their canoes with skins. The practice of sleeping under the canoe which is noted in the saga was also observed by Cartier in the sixteenth century.

Many have tried to trace Norse influence on the languages, myths, and customs of the Indians, but all such efforts have been dilettantish and fantastic. These savages were certainly in no mood to be influenced by the Norse invaders. After the first peaceful meetings, the whole relationship was sealed in bloody combat. The Norsemen might win a skirmish, but their iron weapons could not offset their tremendous inferiority in numbers. They lacked the crushing advantage which firearms conferred on later European invaders of America.

The question has been asked: if the Norsemen discovered America, why did they not settle it as well? Karlsevni answered that question already in the eleventh century: " Even though the country was richly endowed by nature, they would always live in dread and turmoil because of the enmity of those who lived there before." This, and nothing else, was the cause of the abrupt end of Norse colonization in America. Always on the lookout for profitable lands, ready to push on into the wilderness if life were possible there, they got as far as Greenland. Here they stood on the threshold of a land of promise such as no Scandinavian had ever before seen, and they were full of the wonder of it; they called it Vinland, and added an epithet, " the Good." But between them and this dream stood an implacable reality, the hostile peoples of America. The American Indian succeeded in beating off these first European invaders in a skirmish that was a tiny curtain raiser to the great battle of later ages.

The Norsemen in Greenland and Iceland told their children the strange story of Vinland, but the impulse to expansion was gone. In the course of time even the landmarks of the journey grew faint in their memories, for these things need to be kept alive by continuous and repeated sailings. Scattered efforts were made to maintain contact, at least with Markland, where timber could be fetched. A bishop sailed out to seek the lost souls of the heathen. But nothing came of it; the chance of the vikings to be something more than a flash in the pan of world history had come and gone, never to return.

WHERE WAS VINLAND?

The search for Vinland has exercised a strange fascination on men's minds. Both lay and learned have spent many eager hours trying to decipher the mystery of Vinland. Discussion has gone merrily on ever since the Norse sources were rediscovered, and the geography of the American continent more fully explored. Even sober scholars have been given to extravagant and unfounded assertions when dealing with this topic. Yet it must be granted that in a century of study much useful information has been turned up to throw light on the problem. Philologists, historians, astronomers, naval experts, geographers, botanists, and just plain enthusiasts have worked hand in hand towards its clarification. No wholly satisfactory solution is in sight, and until some one undertakes a more searching investigation of the entire Atlantic seaboard than has yet been made, the problem seems to have been pushed as far as the sources permit.

At first blush the Vinland sagas seem remarkably precise and detailed. They give distances and directions, descriptions of the lands visited, and numerous details concerning their climate, their flora and fauna, and their native inhabitants. Yet in all of these details there is probably not a single one whose identification with recognized places and phenomena on the American coast has not been disputed. Not one of the numerous names in the sagas has been identified with such certainty that it has won general recognition among students of the subject. Vinland, the most important, has by competent scholars been located in such various places as Newfoundland (Hovgaard), the mouth of the St. Lawrence (Steensby), Nova Scotia (Storm), northern New England (Thórðarson), Massachusetts (Fiske), Rhode Island (Rafn), New York (Gathorne-Hardy), and Virginia (Mjelde). Most of these identifications are accepted only by their originators, who level at each other bitter charges of distorting the saga text to fit preconceived theories. As a matter of fact, every writer has disregarded something or other in the saga text; if he did not, it would be impossible to identify anything. Still no serious student takes the attitude of the Canadian journalist who boldly wrote, " Let us take some liberties with the old sagas, as they weren't accurate anyway." (He was trying to locate Vinland in Hudson Bay!)

For there is one thing on which all who have really studied these sources are agreed: that through the mist of their frequently confusing and inconclusive details we distinguish the outlines of the North American continent. The eastern seaboard is exceedingly long and complicated. Out of the great number of bays and capes and islands which the vikings observed, only a few could be kept in mind. If they made no more than the five voyages recounted in the sagas, their memory could no longer be refreshed by constant traversing of the course, and so distances and directions would naturally become distorted. The intricacy of experience would gradually give way to the simplicity of a good story.

The general resemblance that still remains is too strong to be accidental. They sailed south and southwest from

Greenland; what land could they reach but America? They found a shore that was stony and unprofitable, with high mountains. They sailed on and found a more inviting coast, with low-lying, wooded shores; and still farther to the south, a fair and tempting land, teeming in all the resources that made life possible. Here they found plants and trees that were unfamiliar to them, and natives of a warlike cast, who are too much like American Indians to have been invented. Every one of these statements is found in manuscripts written before any European suspected the existence of America. One of them might have been hit upon by fancy; but no imagination could assemble so surprising an array of coincidences with realities now well known, but then unsuspected. Especially not, if it is true as one distinguished son of Iceland (Finnur Jónsson) has declared, that his countrymen are noted for their lack of imagination!

Out of the mountain of writings on this subject we shall try to sift the most relevant facts and view with unbiased eye the many theories that have been advanced. In brief summary we shall present the details that may have some value in identifying the places visited by the Norsemen. These occur in connection with the voyages of Bjarni Herjulfson (Chapter 2), Leif Ericson (Chapter 4), and Thorvald Ericson (Chapter 5) in the Greenland Saga, and of Thorfinn Karlsevni (Chapters 10–11) in the Karlsevni Saga. Each of these accounts includes some scattered information about sailing directions, distances traversed, topography, latitude, climate, flora and fauna, and the native inhabitants.

SAILING DIRECTIONS. When Bjarni Herjulfson was blown to the American coast on his way from Iceland to Greenland, he sighted first a shore that was marked by small, wooded knolls. Before a southwest wind he sailed

for two days to a second country, which was level, but well
wooded; then three days to a country with high mountains, topped with ice, and then four days to the southern
tip of Greenland. Leif sailed the same course in reverse
order, and for the last leg the direction is given as southwest. Thorvald explored the coast with Leif's camp as a
base, first to the west, then to the north and east. All of
these directions fit excellently with the general southwest
— northeast slope of the American continent. They suggest that the sons of Eric steered an outside course, off the
land. Karlsevni's voyage, on the other hand, started from
the Western Settlement in Greenland and sailed due
south, then southeast; this course would have brought
him to the southern tip of Labrador. From here there are
no sailing directions until he gets to his first winter camp
at Streamfjord; on his excursion to Vinland he sailed
south along the coast and to the east of it. When he returned to find the lost Thorhall, he sailed from Streamfjord north, then west, then apparently south again. These
complicated directions strongly suggest that he had gotten
into the Gulf of St. Lawrence, and skirted the north end
of Nova Scotia. But all the directions are vague, and must
be allowed a good deal of latitude.

DISTANCES. These are everywhere given in terms of
days' sailing (dœgr) . Unfortunately there is vacillation in
Icelandic usage between twelve-hour days and twenty-
four hour days, and there was no accepted equivalent of a
day's sailing in terms of miles. On the basis of distances
given between Norway, Ireland, and Iceland estimates for
a twenty-four hour day's sailing have been made as ap-
proximately 150 nautical miles. On this basis Bjarni could
have made it from New England to Nova Scotia in the two
days given, from Nova Scotia to Newfoundland in three
days, and from Newfoundland to Greenland in four days.

But it looks suspicious that the numbers coincide so neatly with the number of the country visited, and this suspicion is strengthened when we see the distances given in the Karlsevni Saga, which are everywhere " two days," alternating with a " long time." The " two days " is impossible, for nothing could be reached in that time; so the distances of the Karlsevni Saga have to be disregarded entirely, while something can be salvaged from those of the other.

TOPOGRAPHY. The lands sighted show three successive phases, which is clearly a simplification for purposes of narration and memory. The northernmost was characterized by its high mountains and its stony, barren appearance, and was known as Helluland. The Greenland Saga adds that its mountains were topped by glaciers, and that it was an island. To preserve the glaciers, some have moved it to Baffin's Land. But the glaciers may simply be snowcaps, and the whole description sounds most like Labrador. Even Newfoundland is not excluded. The second country was called Markland on account of its great forests. Bjarni adds that it was level, Leif that it had broad, white beaches, and a gently sloping shoreline, Thorfinn that it had an island off the coast to the southeast which they called Bear Isle. The topographic descriptions are vague, because this kind of country was not what the Norsemen were looking for, and no one cared to stay. From Labrador to New England there are so many coasts that would answer this general description that it can hardly be limited to any one stretch. Scholars have placed it in southeastern Labrador (Hovgaard, Steensby, etc.), in Newfoundland (Storm, Babcock), and most commonly in Nova Scotia because of its long, unbroken forest coastline.

Those regions that were actually lived in and explored

are more thoroughly described. Between Markland and
Vinland proper Karlsevni investigated a large region that
is not noticed in the Greenland Saga, except incidentally.
There was a cape called Keelness, and long, sandy beaches
called Wonderstrands because it took so long to pass them.
Later he came to an island and a fjord with violent tidal
currents, called Streamfjord. There were mountains and
beautiful scenery, but severe winter weather and no grapes.
The sandy beaches suggest Massachusetts, but the other
features do not. We are led to the region between Nova
Scotia and Labrador, with its many inlets and tidal currents, its mountains and cold winters. A likely contender
for Wonderstrands is the southern coast of Labrador,
said to be long, low, and monotonous, while Streamfjord may be Chaleur Bay in New Brunswick (Hermannsson). But these are only guesses. To the west of this region one should expect to find a forest wilderness, which
checks well enough with the estuary of the St. Lawrence.

The topography of Vinland proper includes an absence
of mountains (in spite of the Karlsevni Saga). Bjarni saw
small, wooded knolls. Leif found an island to the north of
the mainland, with a channel between it and a cape jutting out to the north. West of the cape were broad shallows.
Here he found a stream flowing into a lake and then into
the sea. Karlsevni also found a landlocked bay with a river
running into it and sand bars outside. Thorvald explored
this shore to the west and found lovely, wooded country,
with white, sandy beaches; the sea was full of islands and
great shallows. This whole topographic description points
unmistakably to the shores of southern New England;
north of this area the coast is generally rocky and jagged.
But the details are not clear enough to specify any particular locality. An intensive search has been made for
landlocked bays and lakes by the sea, but with little real

success; the changes of shoreline over a thousand years are too considerable to make it likely that such impermanent features would still be there. Rafn was intrigued by the coincidence of name between Hop and Mount Hope Bay in Rhode Island, while the irrepressible Horsford insisted on Boston Back Bay and even proved it by digging up the site of Leif's camp at Gerry's Landing!

LATITUDE. Many investigators have hoped that the astronomical observation found in the Greenland Saga (page 21) would help solve the problem. No feature of the story has been more ardently discussed or ingeniously investigated. Leif and his men noticed that the days in Vinland were much longer in winter than they had been in Iceland. They noted specifically that on the shortest day of the year the sun's course ran all the way from a point on the horizon known in Iceland as "dagmálastað," i.e., breakfast point, to another known as "eyktarstað," i.e., afternoon point.

Unfortunately no record has remained to tell us exactly where these points were. A passage in the Icelandic ecclesiastical code gives a definition of "eyktarstað" which has given rise to endless astronomical discussion. The most reliable, but by no means conclusive result of this calculation is that the observation must have been made south of the 49th degree of latitude, which crosses northern Newfoundland. But there is little help in this, for no one can reasonably place Vinland north of Newfoundland. Besides, why should Greenlanders be so amazed at the change in the sun's height just four days' sailing from their own country?

A passage in the *Edda* of Snorri Sturluson has been less considered, but seems much more pertinent. It states that the sun sets at "eyktarstað" *at the beginning of winter* (probably about October 14 in Iceland). This brings out the real bearing of the passage and the only meaning that makes sense from mariners without sextant or compass. They were simply trying to express how much longer the day was in this region than at home, for — just imagine! — here the sun was as high in the *dead of winter* as in Iceland at the *beginning* of winter. It is no precise observation, but rather a general comparison which suggests that they were a goodly distance from home.

CLIMATE. A salient feature of Vinland was its remarkable climate. Karlsevni knew that Streamfjord was not Vinland because of its severe winter. Both versions agree that there was no winter frost, and that the grass hardly withered, so that cattle could graze outdoors, which would be a treat to most Scandinavian cows. Exceptionally, such conditions can be found in many places along the American coast, but are generally improbable until one gets south of Cape Cod. John Fiske asserts that the winter of 1889–1890 was just such a one at Boston, and Gray insists that it is common on Martha's Vineyard. As a permanent feature of the winter climate it is not appropriate north of Virginia. But it is unthinkable that the Norsemen would not have had more and other things to report had they gotten so far south. The substance of this statement is that the winters were very different from those of Greenland, and it made a better story to say that there was *no* snow, than to say that there was some, but not very much snow.

FLORA AND FAUNA. Most of the controversy over the location of Vinland has raged about the flora, particularly the grapes and the unsown wheat. The grapes are the ancient and unvarying characteristic of Vinland, attested by Adam of Bremen, by the name given to the country, and by the unanimous report of the sagas. In both versions the grapes are found by non-Scandinavians, a German in the Greenland Saga, a most improbable pair of Scotchmen in the Karlsevni Saga. Some one had to identify them as grapes, for the Norsemen had probably never seen the fruit growing, though they had long been acquainted with its end product, the proud and aristocratic drink known as wine. It is not surprising that both they and their descendants should have had vague notions about these berries, even to the extent of believing that they grew on trees and could be preserved through the winter for transport in the spring, if this is what the saga really means.

Astonishing attempts have been made to explain away the finding of grapes by scholars who either are skeptical of the veracity of these accounts, or who wish to place Vinland north of the known limit of the grape. It has been suggested that the grapes and the self-sown wheat are merely loans from classic tales about the Fortunate Isles, or that the grape was really the mountain cranberry (Norwegian *tyttebær*), a plant with which every Norseman was and is familiar from childhood. All this in spite of the fact that nearly every explorer of New England and Canada from later times (Cartier, Lescarbot, Denys, Champlain, Hudson) mentions wild grapes as an outstanding feature of these regions. Along the coast the grape has grown wild as far north as Passamaquoddy Bay between Maine and New Brunswick down to this very day and was formerly in extensive household use.

The self-sown wheat of the sagas, also mentioned by Adam of Bremen, has been identified as maize by learned European scholars who obviously never saw that familiar American plant. Correspondingly, a learned American scholar has said that it must have been lyme-grass (elymus arenaria), which grows everywhere in Iceland and Greenland to this day. The likeliest guess is that it was wild rice, which grows as far north as Newfoundland. Whatever the Norsemen saw, it must have been identical with what

Jacques Cartier saw in 1534, when he spoke of " fields of
wild corn " with " ears like rye and the grain like oats "
that " looked as if it had been sown and cultivated."

The mysterious *mosur* tree, which bobs up in both versions, must have been some sort of rare and precious wood.
A Swedish word *masbjörk* and a German *Maserbirke* refer
to veined birch. A drinking bowl spoken of in one saga as
made of this material probably was of the type still seen in
Norway, made from the protuberances or knobs which
grow on birch trees. Fernald believes it was canoe birch,
others that it was bird's eye maple.

Most of the fauna is of little help in determining the
Vinland locale. Everywhere along the coast there is or was
an abundance of fish, including the halibut mentioned in
the Karlsevni Saga. The same is true of the whales caught.
Nor are the woods teeming with animals especially characteristic, even if the word " dyr " is taken to mean specifically " deer." Only the salmon mentioned in the Greenland Saga may be helpful: while today it stays north of
Cape Cod, it formerly ventured as far south as the mouth
of the Delaware.

NATIVES. Even the natives of Vinland have been the
subject of dispute. Because the word " skraeling," used of
them in the sagas, is nowadays applied to the Eskimos,
some have thought that they must have been Eskimos. But
there is absolutely no evidence that Eskimos have ever
lived south of Labrador, and the details of the sagas point
to a more warlike and enterprising race. The word itself
is one of contempt, like " barbarian " or " savage," which
has here been used to translate it. It is derived from a root
which means " dried up " and is found in such words as
Norwegian *skral* " poor, miserable," Icelandic *skræla*
" dry up," *skrælna* " wither." The word *skraeling* itself is
still used in Iceland to mean a barbarian, while in Nor-

wegian dialects it contemptuously refers to a weakling. This was the indiscriminate term applied by the Norsemen to the first savages they met, the Indians of North America, a fine example of European self-esteem. Two centuries later the word was still remembered, but no Greenlander was alive who had seen an Indian. Then it was natural to apply the word to the new savages who started crowding in from the north.

There can accordingly be no doubt that the natives were Indians, perhaps of the now extinct Beothuk or Micmac tribes. But even so they do not help much in localizing our Vinland.

What conclusions can we draw from all these criteria? The evidence may seem confusing, but it points in one direction. The vikings unquestionably coasted down the eastern seaboard of North America. Their descriptions indicate that they had seen Labrador and Newfoundland, the Gulf of St. Lawrence, and Nova Scotia on their way. But their Vinland could not have been any of these, for grapes do not grow north of Passamaquoddy Bay. And it was farther south still, for in this region the winters are too cold. It could hardly be south of Delaware, however, for this is the southern limit of the salmon. All criteria converge on the Middle Atlantic coast from southern New England to Delaware as the promised land of the Norsemen; there is nothing in the sources that permits us to be more specific. We can only say: *somewhere on the south New England or Middle Atlantic coast* Leif Ericson and Thorfinn Karlsevni stepped ashore on the American continent, and saw that it was good.

IN SEARCH OF RELICS

The eyes of Americans were first opened to the Norse discovery of their country by a ponderous tome which issued from the Royal Danish Society of Antiquaries. This magnificent volume was edited by Carl Christian Rafn, secretary of the Society, in 1837 and entitled *Antiquitates Americanae*. It contained the original saga texts, with Latin and Danish translations, but it did not stop there. Rafn was no dry-as-dust scholar; he was a characteristic son of an age full of enthusiasm for all that was old and remote and simple. He had never been in America, but he was convinced that the vikings must have left relics behind on American shores. So sure of this was he that when he got information from American correspondents about ruined towers and inscribed stones, he at once concluded that they were of Norse origin, and included them in his great work. With naïve, childlike delight he accepted everything that came to hand.

Both in their original publication and in a multitude of popularizers Rafn's ideas made a tremendous impact in New England. Higginson writes, " I can well remember, as a boy, the excitement produced among the Harvard professors when the ponderous volume made its appearance on the library table." New England's hallowed coasts became doubly sacred as the scene of fascinating viking exploits. Rafn's unhesitating identifications of the very spots where the Norsemen had landed were food for the imagination such as New England had never known. Prominent men delivered lectures on the subject, and poets were touched by this evidence of white life long before the pilgrims.

An age was bound to follow in which Rafn's uncritical identifications produced a reaction of disbelief, as these were gradually shown to be wrong. A suspicion grew up in many minds that the whole story was mere froth, because its early advocates had tried to prove too much.

These doubts have been fully set to rest by the labors of a generation of more critical scholars, led by the Norwegian historian Gustav Storm. In his essay, *Studies in the Vinland Voyages,* published in 1887, he tried to clear away some of the debris by distinguishing sharply between fact and fiction. He reacted vigorously against Rafn's uncritical acceptance of everything that might be connected with the Norse discovery. Storm's study challenged others to examine the problem anew, so that today a whole literature of sound scholarship has grown up around the subject. These studies have made the position of the Norse discoveries in world history clearer and more assured. But they have also dissipated some of the many fictions that once grew luxuriantly around the discovery.

While these fictions have been dissipated in the eyes of scholars, many of them linger on in the popular mind. The Norse voyages to America have carried an imaginative appeal to the American public which has affected scholar, poet and layman alike. The general ignorance of the sources and facts in the case has surrounded them with obscurity and mystery.

We have seen how vague and uncertain are the conclusions that can be reached about the location of Vinland;

but the sources do not permit a conscientious student to be more specific. If only the Norsemen had been so considerate as to leave behind a few authentic relics! There are plenty in Greenland; that there should be none in America has seemed too harsh and disappointing a fact to many enthusiastic souls, who have thrown all their energies into the search for Norse remains on the American continent.

We may be sure that if the Norsemen had been able to gain any sort of lasting foothold in America, there would have been authentic remains. But the sagas give us no warrant to believe that they established residences here. The sagas tell us a story of failure; they would not have forgotten a success. The brief winter residences of the vikings can hardly be expected to have left permanent traces.

In spite of this fact the spinning of fictions goes merrily on. It started with the enthusiastic and romantic Rafn, was encouraged by the New England poets, and an army of amateur archeologists; in modern times it has experienced a revival among the Norwegian immigrants of the Middle West. We are here faced with an intensely interesting chapter in the cultural history of America, which still awaits its chronicler. It bears testimony to the human desire for certainty and conviction, and to the perennial fascination of the viking discovery.

Rafn's most important piece of evidence that the landfall of the Norsemen had been in New England was a stone generally known as the Dighton Writing Rock, near Dighton, Massachusetts. This had been observed as early as 1680, and noticed with interest by such famous men as Cotton Mather and the English philosopher George Berkeley. The earliest theory was that its inscriptions had been made by Phoenician visitors to America. In 1789 a copy of it was shown to George Washington, who " smiled, and said he believed the learned Gentlemen were mistaken: and added, that as he had so often examined the rude way of writing practised by the Indians of Virginia, he had no doubt the inscriptions were made, long ago, by some natives of America."

Rafn accepted the stone as of Norse origin, though he had never seen it, and on the basis of crude drawings even managed to read a legend in runes, the old Scandinavian alphabet, saying that " Thorfinn and his 151 men took possession of the land." His imaginative assistant, Finn Magnusen, found pictured on it the prow of a ship, a dismantled vessel, a shield, and a heifer lying down. With a liberal use of fancy he worked this into a design representing " Thorfinn's ship, with his wife seated on the stone, holding in her hand the key of the conjugal dwelling; beside her their three-year-old son. A cock is crowing. Then suddenly approaching war is indicated; Thorfinn seizes his shield, tries to protect himself against the approaching Skrælings, who assail the Norsemen armed with clubs or branches, bows and arrows." He modestly adds that " certain other features of the inscription must be left unexplained."

From imaginative scholar to imaginative poet is not a long step, and we are not surprised that this theory made the Dighton Rock celebrated in song and story. P. C. Sinding was moved to write these fervid lines:

> No shore to which the Northmen came
> But kept some token of their fame;
> On the rough surface of a rock,
> Unmoved by time or tempest's shock,
> In Runic letters, Thorwald drew —
> A record of his gallant crew;
> And these rude letters still are shown
> Deep chiseled in the flinty stone.

A greater poet, Sidney Lanier, alluded to it in his famous " Psalm of the West," when he pictured the Norsemen as the first American settlers. He placed Leif's camp on the Taunton River, where lies the Dighton Rock:

> Then Leif, bold son of Eric the Red,
>   To the South of the West doth flee —
> Past slaty Helluland is sped,
>   Past Markland's woody lea,
> Till round about fair Vinland's head,
>   Where Taunton helps the sea,
>
> The Norseman calls, the anchor falls,
>   The mariners hurry a-strand:
> They wassail with fore-drunken skals
>   Where prophet wild grapes stand;
> They lift the Leifsbooth's hasty walls
>   They stride about the land —

One American poet, however, remained unimpressed, and made delightful satire out of the whole business. In his Biglow Papers, Second Series (1862), James Russell Lowell pretended to turn the interests of his naïve antiquarian parson, Homer Wilbur, M.A., to the subject of Norse inscriptions. Wilbur announces with great excitement that he has found a hitherto unknown " runick inscription " on the east bank of Bushy Brook in North Jaalam. He solemnly explains that there are three kinds of " runick inscriptions," " 1. Those which are understood by the Danish Royal Society of Northern Antiquaries, and Professor Rafn, their Secretary; 2. Those which are comprehensible only by Mr. Rafn; and 3. Those which neither the Society, Mr. Rafn, nor anybody else can be said in any definite sense to understand, and which accordingly offer peculiar temptations to enucleating sagacity.

These last are naturally deemed the most valuable by intelligent antiquaries, and to this class the stone now in my possession fortunately belongs."

Wilbur then goes on to decipher the inscription, chiefly by the process of first making one up and then trying to find it in the characters engraved on the stone; to test its accuracy he turns the stone upside down and finds that it reads exactly the same! This mock inscription informs an eager world that here the Bjarni Grimolfson of our saga (see Chapter 12) " first drank cloud-brother (i.e., tobacco smoke) through child-of-land-and-water (i.e., a reed stem.) " " The Saga, it will be remembered, leaves this Bjarni to (his) fate . . . on board a sinking ship. . . . It is doubly pleasant, therefore, to meet with this proof that the brave old man arrived safely in Vinland, and that his declining years were cheered by the respectful attentions of the dusky denizens of our then uninvaded forest. . . ."

Lowell's satire was a just one, and well deserves reading in full. Washington's belief that the Indians had a hand in the stone has been confirmed by later research; but others, too, explorers and fishermen of modern times, have here left their mark. The Norsemen alone are utterly innocent of any connection with the stone.

Another piece of evidence accepted by Rafn was a ruined tower at Newport, Rhode Island, which he asserted was built in a style of architecture found in twelfth-century Scandinavia. He believed that it was part of an Icelandic chapel, although no chapel built in this style has ever been found either in Iceland or Greenland. After a time it was shown that this tower had once been a windmill, built by Governor Arnold about 1675.

In 1831 a skeleton was uncovered near Fall River, Massachusetts, with a brass breast-plate, a quiver of brass arrows, and a brass belt. Unfortunately it was burned before it could be examined by experts, but there is no reason to believe that it had not belonged to a quite ordinary Indian. In the general excitement over Rafn's book, however, some were ready to see even this as a viking relic. One day in 1838 Henry Wadsworth Longfellow, who was deeply interested in Scandinavia, was riding on the seashore at Newport and got the idea of connecting the Newport tower with the skeleton. To him these were not matters of belief, but they furnished him the theme of a poem on the Norse discovery. This was the "Skeleton in Armor," a rollicking but extremely un-Scandinavian ballad, which tells the story of a viking lover and his maiden.

Hollow-eyed and gaunt, the viking rises from his grave to haunt the poet and make him tell his tale: " I was a Viking old! " Born " by the wild Baltic's strand," he " wooed the blue-eyed maid." But alas, " she was a Prince's child, I but a Viking wild." So the only way he could have his desire was to flee with her across the sea: " Through the wild hurricane, Bore I the maiden."

> " Three weeks we westward bore,
>   And when the storm was o'er
>   Cloud-like we saw the shore
>   Stretching to leeward;
>   There for my lady's bower
>   Built I the lofty tower,
>   Which to this very hour,
>   Stands looking seaward.

> " There lived we many years;
>   Time dried the maiden's tears;
>   She had forgot her fears,
>   She was a mother;

Death closed her mild blue eyes,
Under that tower she lies;
Ne'er shall the sun arise
    On such another!

" Still grew my bosom then,
Still as a stagnant fen!
Hateful to me were men,
    The sunlight hateful!
In the vast forest here,
Clad in my warlike gear,
Fell I upon my spear,
    Oh, death was grateful!

" Thus, seamed with many scars,
Bursting these prison bars,
Up to its native stars
    My soul ascended!
There from the flowing bowl
Deep drinks the warrior's soul,
Skoal! to the Northland! *Skoal!* "
    Thus the tale ended.

A desperate attempt to find the exact location of Leif's landfall was undertaken in the late eighties by a one-time Harvard professor of chemistry, Eben Horsford (1818– 1893), who had made a fortune from the sale of Horsford's Acid Phosphate, a popular nerve tonic. He spent thousands of dollars trying to prove that Leif's landlocked lake was none other than Boston Back Bay. At Gerry's Landing he dug up what he claimed to be the site of Leif's camp, with a ring of charred stones in the middle. He brought over two Icelandic scholars to investigate it for him, and although they declared that no certainty could be reached, Horsford placed a tablet on the spot announcing it as a fact. He was also intrigued by the similarity of Norum-

bega, now a suburb of Boston, to the name of Norway,
and in 1889 erected a tower there to the memory of the
Norse discoverers. His etymological fancies went even further, to the derivation of the name America from that of
Eric the Red, by way of some Indians living in Central
America! But Horsford's enthusiasm went unrewarded;
he found no followers, and today his expensive monuments and his beautifully illustrated volumes are mere
curiosities. We must conclude, in the words of Whittier,
that

> Norumbega proved again
> A shadow and a dream.

The Dighton Rock was not the only inscribed stone
known to Rafn's generation. At Tiverton and Portsmouth
in Rhode Island there are several rocks which excited the
fantasy of the learned Danes. When they found a hook that
looked like a runic L, they naturally assumed that Leif
had here left his initial, while anything like a T they took
to be a reminiscence of Tyrker! In the words of Professor
Delabarre: " It is an example of solemn silliness posing as
serious science." From the study of these and a large number of other such rocks along the Atlantic seaboard it has
gradually emerged that the Indians practised a rude sort
of rock carving, which never reached the level of alpha-
betic writing, but consisted of crude human figures, rep-
resentations of common objects, and just meaningless
scrawls. Nearly all of these rocks have at some time fed the
dream of finding Norse remains on the Atlantic seaboard.

Whittier humorously alluded to one of them in his
poem, " The Double-Headed Snake of Newbury," a stone
at West Newbury, Massachusetts, whose inscription has
turned out to be nothing but natural cracks in the rock.
He says of a mythical two-headed snake investigated by
Cotton Mather, that he does not know

Whether he lurked in the Oldtown fen
Or the gray earth-flax of the Devil's Den,
Or swam in the wooded Artichoke,
Or coiled by the Northman's Written Rock . . .

A fragment of stone found at Bradford, Massachusetts, and shaped something like a human foot, was imagined by some to be the remains of a Norse statue. This gave occasion to Whittier's poem " The Norsemen," in which he calls it

Gift from the cold and silent Past!
Who from its bed of primal rock
First wrenched thy dark, unshapely block?

A spell is in this old gray stone,
My thoughts are with the Past alone!

What sound comes up the Merrimac?
What sea-worn barks are those which throw
The light spray from each rushing prow?
Have they not in the North Sea's blast
Bowed to the waves the straining mast?

Bared to the sun and soft warm air,
Streams back the Norsemen's yellow hair.
I see the gleam of axe and spear,
The sound of smitten shields I hear,
Keeping a harsh and fitting time
To Saga's chant and Runic rhyme.

The wolf beneath the Arctic moon
Has answered to that startling rune;
The Gael has heard its stormy swell,
The light Frank knows its summons well;
Iona's sable-stoled Culdee
Has heard it sounding o'er the sea,
And swept, with hoary beard and hair,
His altar's foot in trembling prayer!

In 1926 a rock finally turned up with undeniable runes on it, a stone on No Man's Land off the Massachusetts coast. Here was the name of Leif Ericson with the date " MI " (1001) and some obscure letters which were interpreted as " Vinland." Unfortunately the Icelanders in the year 1001 were not much inclined to make runic inscriptions on stone; they could hardly have known the Roman method of numbering; and they would not have used either the runes or the spellings of this inscription. It is much more likely that it was made by one of Leif's modern admirers than by Leif himself.

The most ambitious runic stone in all America, however, is one that has practically no connection with the Vinland voyages, and is amazingly remote from the Atlantic seaboard. This is the Kensington Stone, found in 1898 near Alexandria, Minnesota. It was promptly dismissed as a fraud, and universally so regarded until its cause was championed by Mr. Hjalmar Ruud Holand, now a resident of Ephraim, Wisconsin. It contains a long, narrative inscription of a kind never seen in Scandinavia, written in a strange kind of Swedo-Norwegian, with most unorthodox runic characters, all chiseled with meticulous precision. It is dated 1362 and tells the tale of a party of Swedes and Norwegians " on a journey of exploration from Vinland to the west."

Mr. Holand has presented some very plausible arguments in its favor; he has shown that it is not lightly to be dismissed. His notable talent of persuasion and his charm of manner have won him a great following, to whom this is a sacred stone. But he has not yet succeeded in winning over any first-rate authority on runes or medieval Scandinavian languages. The Scandinavian authorities are, in fact, unnecessarily sniffish about it, which may be partly due to a common European suspicion of American frauds.

As the Scotsman Samuel Laing once wrote apropos the Dighton Rock, " The Americans dearly love a little hoax." But the suspicion of the authorities is also due to the strange nature of the stone itself, its message, its language, its runes, its location, and the circumstances of its discovery. Whether one regards it as spurious or genuine, however, its undeniable presence in Alexandria, Minnesota, is very hard to explain. If it is a hoax, it has not yet been unmasked; if it is a voice from the past, its title to speak is still in doubt.

It has encouraged a search for Norse relics in the Middle West as intense as that in New England of an earlier day. In recent years axes and spear points and other objects have been turning up as regularly as runic rocks once did in New England. Supposed Norse relics have been dug out of American soil in widely scattered parts of the Middle West, and the Mandan Indians of North Dakota are claimed as viking offspring. Many of these relics are interesting enough, but none of them have been dug up under conditions that positively eliminated fraud or misconceptions. They are not so distinctive that some other explanation cannot be given of their origin. Nor has it yet been explained why the Norsemen should take any interest in exploring the interior of our continent; their entire lives were lived along the coast, and while they were skilled seamen, they were poor land travellers.

The last few years have indeed seen a whole crop of books which claim to cast light on certain phases of these questions, but which only seem to add to the darkness. One writer proclaims in a book entitled " The Viking and the Red Man " that half the vocabulary of the Algonquin language was derived from Old Norse. The evidence seems impressive until one discovers that the forms given are misquoted and misunderstood, and that the methods of

comparison are unscientific and antiquated. Another en-
thusiast fixes upon Portsmouth Harbor as the Streamfjord
of our saga and publishes a beautifully illustrated book
with the reassuring title " The Truth about Leif Ericsson." He proceeds on the premise that the sagas tell " nothing but the truth," even though he does not know whether
the characters of the saga " could themselves write in long
hand." A third contributor to the folklore of the Norse discoveries has located runic inscriptions up and down the
New England coast by an ingenious technique of inter-
preting geometrical designs on axes and scratches on stones
as secret runes.

It is apparent that the Norse discovery has played an
important rôle in the affections and imaginations of the
American people. Norwegian-Americans have appropri-
ated Leif Ericson from the Icelanders as a kind of national
saint, a symbol of group assertion. But even among old-
stock Americans these early viking explorers have been
enveloped in an intensely romantic haze. Scandinavians
and Americans alike whose enthusiasm has been unham-
pered by a critical sense have seen vast perspectives of
forgotten Norse colonies in the American wilderness, a regular Norse empire stretching from Massachusetts to Minnesota. They have more or less unconsciously wanted to
magnify the importance of the Norse discoveries. Scandinavians could not understand that their ancestors missed
so great an opportunity, and Americans have been puzzled
that any one could see our grand country and remain so
uninterested.

While most or all of these attempts to find Norse relics
on American soil are clearly will-o'-the-wisps, they have
been a boon to poets and a stimulus to American imagi-
nativeness. Many have felt a gratitude for these relics

which was best expressed by Whittier in his poem " The Norsemen ":

> Yet, for this vision of the Past,
> This glance upon its darkness cast.
> My spirit bows in gratitude
> Before the Giver of all good,
> Who fashioned so the human mind,
> That from the waste of Time behind,
> A simple stone, or mound of earth,
> Can summon the departed forth;
> Quicken the Past to life again,
> The Present lose in what hath been,
> And in their primal freshness show
> The buried forms of long ago.

RESULTS AND SIGNIFICANCE

The Norse discoveries set up strangely few reverberations in world history. We have seen why they fell short of permanence; but this does not explain why so little knowledge of them filtered through to the rest of Europe. At the time of the actual discoveries there was intimate knowledge of them in Greenland, and pretty full information available in Iceland. People in Norway must have known about them, and we see that soon after the middle of the eleventh century the news got as far as Denmark. Very much abbreviated and garbled it reached the rest of Europe in Adam of Bremen's ponderous work. Why did this news fail to stir the European imagination and awaken the spirit of enterprise?

The real reason was that in the year 1000 Europe was not ready to discover America. Europe and Scandinavia consisted of a mass of petty states, bickering and fighting among themselves and wholly occupied with internal problems. The kings were often nominal or temporary heads, whose authority was none too secure. None of the European nations was very old, and they were just beginning to acquire some slight stability. Four hundred years later they had grown large and strong; kings sat securely on their thrones as the wielders of unlimited power, with huge national treasuries at their command. England, France, Spain, and Portugal had accumulated large capitals which could be used to finance expeditions of exploration and settlement. Firearms made the subjugation of native populations easy. Even so, it took the European imperialists a century of heartbreaking failures before they gained a secure foothold on this continent.

The rise of the larger nations of southern and central Europe coincided with a decline in the fortunes of the small ones in the North. Just as the new age of exploration and enlightenment was about to dawn in the rest of Europe, the Greenland settlements were disintegrating. Iceland lost her sovereignty in 1262, and much of her cultural vigor in the century that followed. The sagas passed out of oral tradition, and settled into the comparative obscurity of the manuscripts. These were still retained, and frequently copied, but had to compete in the interests of the people with foreign romances. Norwegian cultural life was struck a drastic blow by the Black Death and the successive unions with Sweden and Denmark during the fourteenth century. Linguistic changes isolated Norway from Iceland, and after the union of Calmar in 1397 both countries gradually fell under the dominance of the Danish crown. All of these countries became marginal with respect to Europe, for they had no center of gravity within themselves to assert their ancient traditions. When the age of exploration came, no one looked to them for information about great discoveries. Meanwhile the story of Vinland gathered dust in the archives of Iceland.

Then one day in 1492 a Genoese sailor with the fixed idea that he could sail west to reach the Indies ran across the same continent that Leif had skirted five centuries before. After Columbus came a horde of explorers and conquistadores to plant the flags of Spain, Portugal, England,

and France in its virgin soil. A new world had emerged, to which all Europe must orient its existence.

But the connection between this new world and the ancient explorations of the Northmen remained unknown and almost unsuspected, even in Iceland. Those who had not forgotten about Greenland thought of it as lying " at the western boundary of Europe " and they did not get much enlightenment from Adam of Bremen's old history when it was first printed in 1595. Throughout the sixteenth century the Danish kings tried vainly to re-establish the contact with Greenland. Not until the seventeenth century did intimations begin to bob up of a renewed knowledge of the old northern route. The geographer Ortelius wrote in 1601 that the inhabitants of Iceland and Greenland must have been the first to discover America; a Danish clergyman alluded to Vinland in a bit of doggerel verse from 1608; the famous Dutch jurist, Hugo Grotius, credited the Norsemen with the discovery of America in 1642, and even maintained that the Indians were their descendants. King Christian IV of Denmark sent a series of expeditions to Greenland soon after 1600, and in 1619 he sent Jens Munk to discover the Northwest Passage, but apparently without any realization that Scandinavians had sailed these waters before.

The real story of Vinland had to come from Iceland herself. In 1643 the scholarly Arngrimur Jónsson, who had latinized his name to Arngrimvs Ionas, issued his *Specimen Islandiæ historicum* in Amsterdam. Here the ancient saga was for the first time interpreted in the light of the new discoveries. The original manuscripts were still hidden away in Iceland; but about this time they began migrating out of their old repositories by the native hearth to the royal libraries of Denmark. It remained for the most learned Icelander of his day to give the world the full

text of the sagas. This was the robust Thormod Torfaeus, who was employed by the King of Denmark as Royal
Historiographer of Norway.

Torfaeus published in 1705 the first complete account
of the discovery in a work that was written in Latin and
won a wide circulation in Europe. In the course of his
work he dropped more than a hint to the King of Denmark that these discoveries gave him the right to claim a
part of the North American continent. Everyone else was
getting colonies, why should not Denmark? But it was too
late. Stronger powers had already established themselves
in America, and Torfaeus' book remained of purely academic interest. This dream of American colonies haunted
the Danish mind even a century later, when another
scholar, Finn Magnusen, declared " that if the Icelandic
language . . . had been understood at the Danish court
three hundred years ago, our country might now perhaps
have been one of Europe's mightiest states and the world
might have looked quite different from now."

But these regrets were idle, and the Danish crown never
tried to assert its domain farther than Greenland, which
fell to it as a fruit of its union with Norway.

Instead, Danish scholars once tried to show that there
was a vital connection between the Norse discoveries and
the later feats of Christopher Columbus. The idea was
first suggested by a Danish geographer, Malte-Brun, in
1812. A year later it was taken up by Finn Magnusen, who
discovered that Columbus claimed to have made a voyage
into the Iceland seas in 1477; Magnusen believed that on
this voyage he met Icelanders who could have told him
about the Norse voyages. This appealing idea was accepted
by Rafn and others, and was made much of by certain
American writers. In this way the idea, which started as a
scholar's fancy, has become almost a popular dogma. The

notion that Leif Ericson and Christopher Columbus should have touched hands across the centuries is so dramatic that it carries almost immediate conviction. In a poem of 1844 James Russell Lowell represented Columbus as saying:

> I brooded on the wise Athenian's tale
> Of happy Atlantis, and heard Björne's keel
> Crunch the gray pebbles of the Vinland shore . . .

Unfortunately this is another of the attractive but illusory will-o'-the-wisps that surround the theme of Vinland. Adam of Bremen's account would hardly have tempted Columbus to seek out this " island " to the north of Greenland, one day's sail from the frozen icepack. No evidence has made it probable that there remained any information in fifteenth-century Rome concerning Vinland. This leaves us only one possible connection, suggested by a note Columbus is claimed to have written. This is quoted by his son Fernando and begins " In the month of February 1477 I sailed a hundred leagues beyond the island of Tile . . ." As this Tile must have been Thule, a medieval name for Iceland, this opens a vista of possible connections which have been utilized to the full.

But the whole structure is based on a series of far-fetched assumptions, every one of which has to be true to prove the point. We have to assume that Columbus really wrote this note (which is disputed by many) ; that if so, he was telling the truth (he was not above boasting now and then about things he had not done) ; that if he went to Iceland, he got most of his facts wrong; that he never again mentioned having been there; that he did not just sail past Iceland, as the note clearly says, but went on shore; that he was able to find natives handy who could talk Latin; that he happened to ask the natives about Vinland, and found some one who had read the rare, ancient manuscripts that told about it; that the products of Vinland (grapes, wheat, furs) seemed attractive enough to be worth bothering about by a man who was dreaming of the silks and spices of the Indies; that in all his impassioned speeches to the rulers of Europe, trying every means to persuade them that there was land to the west, he failed to use this argument; and most mysterious of all, that knowing about the location of Vinland, he sailed in an almost exactly opposite direction, far to the south!

The latest effort to bridge all these gaps of missing evidence flows from the incisive pen of Vilhjalmur Stefansson, famous arctic explorer. He believes in a widespread plot on the part of Pope and Spaniards to suppress knowledge of the Norse discoveries and their effect on Columbus. This theory has the admirable virtue of explaining everything without being in the least capable of proof. One wonders just how much Spain really had to fear from possible counterclaims to the American continent by the Danish king. Stefansson is more successful in his attempts to establish the possibility of Columbus's visit to Iceland. He shows that Columbus's statements about Iceland are not as absurd as some have thought and that his biographers are more reliable than they seem. But he does not show that the obvious medieval familiarity with Greenland carried with it a knowledge of Vinland, or that Columbus in any way added to his stock of information on this subject by his presumed voyage to Iceland. There is still that hurdle which stopped Gustav Storm, who believed that Columbus had been to Iceland, but could find no effect of this voyage on his American discoveries. Stefansson proceeds to count noses among previous writers on the subject, but the fact that a majority have believed in Columbus's voyage to Iceland proves very little when we begin to consider the quality of some of those noses.

Even though the Norse voyages could hardly have had any significance for Columbus, it is not impossible that some oral knowledge of lands to the west circulated among the seamen of the North. There was much eager search- ing for information about the unknown West in England in the fifteenth century, and it is striking that John Cabot started from the port of Bristol, which was the center of an illicit English trade with Iceland, and not improbably with Greenland. But these problems will remain forever insoluble, unless new documents turn up to settle them.

The claim of the Norse discoveries to world interest does not lie in their influence on later voyages, or on the course of world history. It lies in their own intrinsic value. They give American history a colorful opening, a series of vivid scenes and characters which we should otherwise have missed. They bring America into contact with one of the most fascinating cultures of the old world, that of Scandinavia in the viking age. They constitute the first recorded feelers extended by Europeans towards a new world of promise in the west. These early explorers and settlers were filled with the same longing for wider oppor- tunities as the later ones, and they had to face the same problems of sustenance and protection. The Norse vikings were the first American pioneers, and as such they deserve an honorable place in the pageant of American history.

When the first Norwegian emigrants of modern times began coming to America about a century ago, they were at once moved by the parallel between their course and that of the ancient discoverers of America. The first poem known to have been composed by such an emigrant, writ- ten on the Atlantic in 1837, struck the note that has re- echoed among Norwegian-Americans for more than a hundred years:

As ocean waves in ancient days
Oft cradled sturdy viking boats,
So troubled seas and fiercest storms
Can strike no fear in Norsemen's hearts.
And so to-day Norwegians greet
The distant shore of Vinland the Good.

The knowledge that their ancestors were the first to visit these shores has always given Scandinavian immigrants a special bond with America. But for them the story was tinged with sadness, too, for (in the words of the Norwegian historian, P. A. Munch) if the vikings had been successful, " Scandinavian settlers, with Scandinavian language and nationality, would perhaps have played the same rôle in America as the English and their descendants to-day."

The unwillingness of some American historians of an older school to grant full recognition of the Norse discovery in American textbooks has always been a disturbing fact to Americans of Scandinavian origin. As custodians of Leif Ericson's honor, they have felt themselves compelled to agitate for such recognition. The first book published by a Norwegian in this country on a scholarly topic was an effort to convert Americans to the Scandinavian way of thinking. This was the challenging and pugnacious little book entitled *America Not Discovered by Columbus*, written in 1874 by Rasmus B. Anderson, first professor of Scandinavian languages at the University of Wisconsin. The book was a mere uncritical summary of the arguments of Rafn, but it won a wide audience, and led eventually to a movement for the official recognition of Leif Ericson as the proper discoverer of America.

The first fruit of Anderson's agitation was the unveiling in Boston of a Leif Ericson statue by Anne Whitney on October 29, 1887. The original plan had been that An-

derson and the great Norwegian violinist Ole Bull should
gather funds in the Middle West and place the statue on
the Campus of the University of Wisconsin. But this came
to naught, and the idea was taken over by a committee
of prominent Bostonians, including the authors Holmes,
Lowell, and Longfellow. On November 15, 1887, a replica
of this statue was set up in Juneau Park, Milwaukee, by
Mrs. J. F. Gilbert, a wealthy lady of that city whose interest is said to have been in the statue, not the discovery.
In the late eighties a statue of Leif by Sigvald Asbjørnsen
was erected in Humboldt Park, Chicago. A monument of
Thorfinn Karlsevni by Einar Jónsson was unveiled in
Fairmount Park, Philadelphia, on November 20, 1920.
In 1930 the United States Congress donated a ten-foot
statue of Leif Ericson by A. Stirling Calder to Iceland on
the occasion of its millennial celebration of statehood. A
painting of Leif Ericson discovering America, copied
from the work of the Norwegian painter Christian Krogh,
hangs in the halls of Congress, a gift from Norwegians to
the United States, presented on March 23, 1936. A square
in Brooklyn, a street in Chicago, parks everywhere have
been named after Leif Ericson.

There has even been a strenuous effort to consecrate a
special day to his memory. It became common in the
nineties for Norwegian-American organizations to cele-
brate the memory of the discoverers some time in the fall,
when the grapes began to ripen. In 1923 an organization
known as the Leif Ericson Memorial Association was cre-
ated, and October 9 selected as its date. In states with large
Scandinavian populations this day has been officially recognized as a day to be observed in the public schools.
The first state to adopt it was Wisconsin, on May 10, 1929;
the next was Minnesota, in April, 1931; others have followed their example. In one year, 1935, it was even recog-

nized by the Congress of the United States, as a day of tribute to the Scandinavian element in our population.

In spite of the fulsome veneration with which the figure of Leif Ericson has often been surrounded, and his elevation to a kind of Norwegian sainthood, the story of the sagas lives on as one of the great epics of exploration. It is a courageous tale of human hopes and aspirations, capable of being enjoyed without any regard to its results or its significance.

NOTES AND INDEX

NOTES AND REFERENCES

So many excellent books have been drawn upon in the preparation of this survey that it is a pleasure to list some of them here. These will offer ideas and material for any interested reader who may wish to pursue the subject further. For more complete bibliographies of the Vinland voyages one should turn to Halldór Hermannsson's *The Northmen in America* (Ithaca, New York, 1909) and A. W. Brøgger's *Vinlandsferdene* (Oslo, 1937). The most comprehensive and unbiased piece of scholarship in the field is *The Finding of Wineland the Good* by Arthur Middleton Reeves (London, 1890), a stately work presenting phototypic reproductions of the original manuscripts with complete translations and documentation. To this the reader is constantly and enthusiastically referred. Gratitude is also due Professor Halvdan Koht for valuable oral suggestions.

FOREWORD. Page vi: The Holiday Press version appeared in 1941 in an edition limited to 350 copies; it was specially prepared by a group of craftsmen, employes of the Lakeside Press, who have made it their hobby to produce fine books. Page vi: The original manuscripts are now available in a newer reproduction than that of Reeves in the impressive series *Corpus Codicum Islandicorum Medii Aevi*, published in Copenhagen by Ejnar Munksgaard. The *Flateyjarbók* appeared in 1930 (introduction by Finnur Jónsson) and the *AM 557 4to* in 1940 (introduction by Dag Strömbäck). Page vi: Samuel Laing's translation of the Greenland Saga appeared originally in the appendix of his *Heimskringla; or the Chronicle of the Kings of Norway* (London, 1844) and was reprinted in *Everyman's Library* (Volume 717) in 1915. Reeves' translation was reprinted in *The Northmen Columbus and Cabot,* edited by Julius Olson (New York, 1906). G. M. Gathorne-Hardy's translation is a part of his *The Norse Discoverers of America* (Oxford, 1921) and was reprinted in A. W. Lawrence and Jean Young, *Narratives of the Discovery of America* (New York, 1931). Page vi: One of the most interesting examples of saga translation is *The Laxdæla Saga* by Thorstein Veblen, famous Norwegian-American economist (New York, 1925).

THE SAGA OF VINLAND. Page 4: The interpretation of "hall-beams" (Old Norse *setstokkar*) is that of Valtýr Guðmundsson, *Privatboligen på Island i Sagatiden* (Copenhagen, 1889), pp. 213–14, 220–21. Others believe that they were the carved posts of the 'high seat' in the hall, but this seems unlikely.

ADAM OF BREMEN. Page 97: Adam of Bremen's *Gesta Hammaburgensis ecclesiæ pontificum* may be read in a German translation by J. C. M. Laurent (Leipzig, 1886); his life and work are discussed in E. Wessén, *Studier til Sveriges hedna mythologi och fornhistoria* (Uppsala, 1924), and in Johannes Steenstrup, *Det danske Folks Historie* (Copenhagen, 1927), Vol. II, page 13. Page 98: Svein Estridsson (ruled 1047–76) is described by Steenstrup in the work just cited, page 9. Page 99: The story of Auðun occurs in *Morkinskinna,* a compilation of sagas about the kings of Norway. Page 99: The 'learned Swedish scholar' was Olof Rudbeck, who published his *Atland eller Manheim* at Uppsala about 1689.

THE LEARNED MEN OF ICELAND. Page 101: For an account of the Christianizing of Iceland see Knut Gjerset, *History of Iceland* (New York, 1924). Page 101: On the runic alphabets see Otto von Friesen, ed., *Runorna* (Stockholm, 1933) and Helmut Arntz, *Handbuch der Runen-*

kunde (Halle, Saale, 1935) . Page 102: Ari fróði's *Íslend-ingabók* has been edited and translated by Halldór Hermannsson in *Islandica,* Vol. XX (Ithaca, New York, 1930) .

VIKING TRADITIONS. Page 105: Good accounts of viking life and civilization are found in T. D. Kendrick, *A History of the Vikings* (New York, 1930) , in Axel Olrik, *Viking Civilization* (New York, 1930) , and in Allen Mawer, *The Vikings* (Cambridge, 1913) . Page 106: The story of Bjorn, son of Brynjolf, is found in *Egil's Saga,* chapter 32, and is supposed to have taken place about 900. Page 108: Old Norse-Icelandic literature is ably summarized in Bertha Phillpotts, *Edda and Saga* (New York, 1931) ; the Sagas in Halvdan Koht, *The Old Norse Sagas* (New York, 1931) and in Knut Liestøl, *The Origin of the Icelandic Family Saga* (Oslo, 1930) . Page 109: Lord Raglan's views are presented in *The Hero* (New York, 1937) , an incisive but somewhat superficial treatment of the problem.

THE TWO VERSIONS. Page 112: See Halldór Hermannsson, *Icelandic Manuscripts* (Ithaca, New York, 1929) . Page 113: What is here known as the " Karlsevni Saga " has since Storm been generally known as the " Saga of Eric the Red "; we are here following the suggestion made by Hermannsson (*Problem of Wineland,* page 29) . Another common name for it is the " Hauksbók Version." The Greenland Saga is generally referred to as either the " Tale of the Greenlanders " or the " Flatey Book Version." Page 114: The only important treatments of the problem here discussed which appeared before Gustav Storm were those of Tormod Torfaeus in 1705 and Carl Christian Rafn in 1837. Storm's monograph appeared in *Aarbøger for nordisk Oldkyndighed* (Copenhagen) , 1887

(English version entitled *Studies on the Vinland Voyages,* 1889). The other discussions will be found listed in the notes to WHERE WAS VINLAND.

THE LAND OF ERIC THE RED. Page 117: The papal letter was issued by Alexander VI and is printed in *Norsk Historisk Tidsskrift* for 1892, page 407; it also appeared in Vol. 16 of the *Norroena* series (1906), edited by Rasmus B. Anderson, where it was claimed to be newly discovered, and to refer to Vinland, neither of which is true. Page 120: An excellent account of the Greenland excavations is available in Poul Nørlund, *Viking Settlers in Greenland* (London, 1936). Many treatises have appeared in *Meddelelser om Grønland* (Copenhagen, 1890 to date). The old, written sources on Greenland are gathered in *Grønlands Historiske Mindesmærker* (3 vols., Copenhagen, 1845). Page 123: King Christiern's plans are revealed by a papal letter of June 20, 1519, which may be found in *Diplomatarium Norvegicum* XVII (1902–13), 1164.

VOYAGES TO VINLAND. Page 129: The eminent specialist in Greenlandic, W. Thalbitzer, has made an effort to interpret the babblings of Karlsevni's savages in terms of Eskimo (*Forhandlinger* of the Danish Scientific Academy, 1905), but without much success. Page 129: On the Freydis incident see Stefán Einarsson in *Acta Philologica Scandinavica* XIII (1938–9), 246–56. Page 131: On Gudrid and the witchcraft scene see Dag Strömbäck, *Sejd* (Stockholm, 1935), 49–60.

WHERE WAS VINLAND? Page 135: The following are some of the most important works which have advanced original theories on the location of Vinland on the basis of sound and admissible evidence: Gustav Storm (previously cited), 1887; John Fiske, *The Discovery of America* (2 vols., Boston, 1892); M. L. Fernald, *Notes on the Plants of Wineland the Good* (*Rhodora,* Vol. 12, Boston, 1910) ; William H. Babcock, *Early Norse Visits to North America* (Smithsonian Miscellaneous Collections, Washington, D. C., 1913) ; William Hovgaard, *The Voyages of the Norsemen to America* (New York, 1914) ; Finnur Jónsson, *Opdagelsen af og Rejserne til Vinland* (*Aarbøger for nordisk Oldkyndighed,* Copenhagen, 1915) ; H. P. Steensby, *The Norsemen's Route from Greenland to Wineland* (*Meddelelser om Grønland,* Copenhagen, 1917) ; G. M. Gathorne-Hardy, *The Norse Discoverers of America* (Oxford, 1921) ; Matthias Thordarson, *The Vinland Voyages* (American Geographical Society, Research Series No. 18, New York, 1930) ; M. Mjelde, *The Norse Discoveries of America* (*Saga-Book of the Viking Society,* London, 1928–29) ; Halldór Hermannsson, *The Problem of Wineland* (Ithaca, New York, 1936) ; A. W. Brøgger, *Vinlandsferdene* (Oslo, 1937). Of historical interest are also the solutions offered by Tormod Torfaeus in *Historia Vinlandiae antiquae, seu partis Americae septentrionalis* (Copenhagen, 1705; English translation, New York, 1891) and by Carl Christian Rafn in *Antiquitates Americanae sive Scriptores Septentrionales Rerum Ante-Columbianarum in America* (Copenhagen, 1837). Page 136: The Canadian journalist is James W. Curran, *Here was Vinland, America's Strangest Story* (Sault Ste. Marie, Canada, 1939). Page 137: The statement by Finnur Jónsson appears in *Den oldnorske og oldislandske Litteraturs Historie* (Copenhagen, 1902) , III, 80. Page 141: On *eyktarstað.* The 49th-degree solution was worked out by the Norwegian astronomer Hans Geelmuyden; a new solution, proposed by M. Mjelde in 1922, brings it down to the 37th degree. Page 143: The theory that these elements were drawn from classic tales of the Fortunate Isles was launched by the great Norwegian explorer Fridtjof Nansen, *In Northern Mists* (London, 1911), but has found little support. Page 143: An etymology of Vinland varying from the usual one, by which *vin* should mean 'meadow,' instead of 'wine' or 'vine,' is impossible for a number of reasons, as shown by Finnur Jónsson in *Norsk Historisk Tidsskrift* (Oslo, 1911). Page 144: the southern limit of the salmon is established from information found in *Check List of the Fishes and Fishlike Vertebrates of North and Middle America* by D. S. Jordan, W. Evermann, H. W. Clark (Document 1055, United States Bureau of Fisheries Report, 1928). Page 144: Etymology of skraeling taken from Alf Torp, *Nynorsk etymologisk ordbok* (Oslo, 1919); it is much to be preferred over the Eskimo origin suggested by Thalbitzer.

IN SEARCH OF RELICS. Page 146: Reeves' comment on Rafn is very apt: ". . . He has seriously qualified the credit to which he is entitled by the extravagant theories and hazardous statements to which he gave currency, and which have prejudiced many readers against the credibility of the records themselves." (*Op. cit.*, 98). Page 146: Thomas W. Higginson wrote in *Harper's Magazine*, 1882 (Vol. 65, 515–27), repeated in his *Larger History of the United States* (New York, 1886), 28–51. Page 148: The Dighton Rock has been made the subject of a brilliant work by Edmund Burke Delabarre, *Dighton Rock. A Study of the Written Rocks of New England* (New York, 1928). Most of the information here given is drawn from his study. Page 151: On the Newport Tower see J. G. Palfrey, *History of New England* (Boston, 1858), 57–9; a picture of a stone mill at Chesterton, England, almost identical to the Newport Tower is reprinted in the Higginson article cited above. At the very time this book goes to press, a new and challenging study of the Newport Tower has just appeared: Philip Ainsworth Means, *Newport Tower* (New York, 1942). This writer, an Associate in

Anthropology at Harvard's Peabody Museum, claims to have destroyed the generally accepted theory, thereby opening the possibility that the tower was not originally a windmill. Although Mr. Means does not assert its viking origin, he believes there is a strong chance that excavations may support this theory. Simultaneously the problem has been attacked by Mr. Holand, who reaches similar conclusions and inevitably attributes the tower to the Paul Knutson expedition, presumably on its way to Minnesota to make the Kensington Stone. Like so many theories of Vinland, these contain more guesswork than fact; but the vistas are undeniably intriguing! Page 153: A description of Horsfords' excavations will be found in his *Leif's Houses in Vinland* (Boston, 1893), one of the many expensive publications which he issued. Page 156: The rock on No Man's Land is discussed and interpreted in Edward F. Gray, *Leif Eriksson, Discoverer of America A.D.* 1003 (New York, 1930); in spite of his great interest in the rock, however, Mr. Gray does not believe that it can be adduced " as scientific evidence to corroborate the view that No Man's Land was the winter headquarters of the Vinland Expeditions." Page 156: The classic presentation of the evidence for the Kensington Stone is Mr. Holand's *Westward from Vinland* (New York, 1940); in spite of its eloquence and undeniable value, it has not cleared away all the objections of scholars. Pages 157–58: The works here referred to are Reider T. Sherwin, *The Viking and the Red Man* (New York, 1940); William B. Goodwin, *The Truth about Leif Ericsson and the Greenland Voyages to New England* (Boston, 1941); Olaf Strandwold, *Runic Rock Inscriptions along the American Atlantic Seaboard* (Prosser, Washington, 1939). An earlier effort of similar validity is Thomas E. Pickett, *The Quest for a Lost Race* (Louisville, Kentucky, 1907).

RESULTS AND SIGNIFICANCE. Page 162: From maps and
treatises it clearly appears that Greenland was believed to
be continuous with the European continent; see Reeves,
Op. cit., 15 ff. Page 162: The early references to Vinland
are gathered in Reeves, *Op. cit.,* 92 ff., and in Georg Fried-
erici, *Der Charakter der Entdeckung und Eroberung
Amerikas durch die Europäer* (Stuttgart, 1936), III, 54.
The Danish clergyman was Claus Lyschander. A transla-
tion of Hugo Grotius's *Dissertatio de origine gentium
Americanarum* appeared in Edinburgh in 1884 (*On the
Origin of the Native Races of America*). Page 162: Jens
Munk's story of his voyage, *Navigatio Septentrionalis,* was
republished and edited by P. Lauridsen (Copenhagen,
1883). Page 163: Finn Magnusen's statement appeared in
Athene (Copenhagen, 1813). Page 163: The story of the
Columbus-Leif Ericson theory is outlined briefly in
Brøgger, *Vinlandsferdene,* 189 ff. (who does not believe
that anything Columbus might have learned from the Ice-
landers would have been of any value to him). Malte-
Brun's theory was tentatively presented in his *Précis de la
géographie universelle* (Paris, 1810 ff.). Lowell's poem is
entitled "Columbus" (*Poetical Works,* 1896, p. 482).
Page 165: This problem is the chief subject matter of
Vilhjalmur Stefansson's *Ultima Thule* (New York, 1940).
Page 166: The latest discussion is in Samuel Eliot Morison, *Admiral of the Ocean Sea* (2 vols., Boston, 1942), I,
32–35; Morison reaches the same conclusion as the one
here presented, previously advanced by the Norwegian
historians Gustav Storm and A. W. Brøgger. But Morison
is in error when he refers to the theory as a " new ' Nordic '
myth "; it is neither new nor specially Nordic. Page 166:
On the likelihood that a Norwegian expedition on Portu-
guese initiative sailed to Labrador in the 1470's see Brøgger, *Vinlandsferdene,* 175 ff.; it is associated with such

names as Pining, Pothorst, and Johannes Scolvus, and is surrounded with much uncertainty. Pages 166–67: The Norwegian-American poem was written by Ole Rynning, and is available in Theodore C. Blegen and Martin B. Ruud, *Norwegian Emigrant Songs and Ballads* (Minneapolis, 1936), 24 ff. Page 167: The quotation from P. A. Munch appeared in *Alumuevennen* (Oslo, 1850). Page 167: The fashion in American textbooks may have been set by George Bancroft, who in his *History of the United States* (Vol. I, 1834) wrote: " The story of the colonization of America by Northmen rests on narratives mythological in form, and obscure in meaning, ancient yet not contemporary."

INDEX

PRINTER'S NOTE

The text of this book was set on the Linotype in Baskerville. The punches for this face were cut under the supervision of George W. Jones, an eminent English printer. Linotype Baskerville is a facsimile cutting from type cast from the original matrices of a face designed by John Baskerville. The original face was one of the forerunners of the "modern" group of type faces.

Typography and binding designs by W. A. Dwiggins. Composed, printed, and bound by The Plimpton Press, Norwood, Massachusetts.